STORAGE

SAN DIEGO PUBLIC LIBRARY

LIBRARY RULES

A Bundle of Ballads

OMIT

(A) Bundle of Ballads

Compiled by

RUTH MANNING-SANDERS

Illustrated by

WILLIAM STOBBS

J. B. LIPPINCOTT COMPANY
Philadelphia   New York

© Ruth Manning-Sanders 1959

Lithographed in the United States of America

LIBRARY OF CONGRESS CATALOG CARD NUMBER 61-6066

Contents

Introduction

Probably everyone knows the story of Richard Cœur de Lion and the minstrel, Blondel: how, when Richard was taken prisoner during the Crusades and no one could find him, Blondel, harp in hand, wandered across Europe from castle to castle, singing under the windows a song that he and Richard had often sung together. Always Blondel paused 'at half the song' to listen; until, one day, from behind the bars of a high-up window, he heard the voice of the king 'begin the other half and complete it'.

Blondel was able to do this because, as a minstrel, he had no enemies; a minstrel was a welcome guest everywhere, and it made no difference whether the country he happened to be passing through was at war with his own country or not. For the same reason, three centuries earlier, King Alfred, disguised as a minstrel, was able to enter the camp of the enemy Danes 'with the utmost security'; there to 'entertain their king at table', and find out the strength of their forces, although the Danes must have known by his accent that Alfred was a Saxon.

People in those far-off days liked stories just as much as people do now; and because they had few books or none, and for the most part could not read, they delighted in the visits of the minstrels, who roamed the country from one great lord's house to another, singing their stories and accompanying themselves on the harp.

The stories the minstrels sang were on familiar themes; stories of well-known battles, of historic raids and captures and daring rescues, of the deeds of bold outlaws, of gallant lovers, and of that mysterious realm of magic that hung like a shimmering mist behind all the busy doings of mankind. Of these old ballads no one can say when any particular one was composed, or who was the author of it. One minstrel, hearing the song from another, would take a fancy to it and sing it again, inventing his own lines when his memory failed him, adding new verses according to his fancy, and perhaps giving the story a slightly different twist to suit his audience.

Moreover, long after these wandering minstrels had ceased to exist, the stories they had sung were remembered by old country folk, who had heard them from their grandfathers and grandmothers in their childhood. The story as it was remembered by an old man in one part of the country, would differ in many details from the story of the same event as remembered by an old woman in another part of the country. So that, when the ballads at last came to be collected and written down, the people who collected them were faced with a bewildering variety of versions of the same story, and had to choose amongst these versions as best they might.

But, amidst all the confusion, there is at least one sure guide—the feeling of the words themselves. As told by the minstrels, the story was swift, vivid, and to the point. Neither singer nor listener had any use for 'pretty-pretty' phrases or elaboration of detail. The story is the thing: and in the telling, the singer leaps rapidly from happening to happening, with no waste of words. So that when one comes across lines put in merely for the sake of ornament, which add nothing to the story itself, one knows such lines to be a corrupt addition invented by some sentimental brain of a later age.

It is the simplicity and directness of these old ballads that give them their unique charm. They have a magic of their own that is unmistakable, and which it is impossible for any modern writer to recapture. Greater poetry has doubtless been written, and will be written, but the poetry of the ballads remains for all time triumphantly inimitable, and, in its own way, perfect.

Being set down in the dialect of the people who spoke them, the ballads are not always easy to understand. So here and there I have modernized words and phrases which I thought might be unintelligible to you; trying to keep always to the spirit of the original, and hoping that you will like them well enough to tackle them by and by in their own dialect, and forget my emendations.

Sir Patrick Spens

The king sits in Dunfermline town,
  Drinking the blood-red wine;
'O where will I get a skeely skipper
  To sail this new ship of mine?'

1

Then up and spake an ancient knight,
    Sat at the king's right knee;
'Sir Patrick Spens is the best sailor
    That ever sailed the sea.'

Our king has written a broad letter,
    And sealed it with his hand,
And sent it to Sir Patrick Spens,
    Was walking on the strand.

'To Noroway, to Noroway,
    To Noroway o'er the foam,
The king's daughter to Noroway,
    'Tis thou must take her home.'

The first word that Sir Patrick read
    So loud, loud laughed he;
The next word that Sir Patrick read
    The tear blinded his e'e.

'O who is this has done this deed
    And told the king of me,
To send us out this time of year
    To sail upon the sea?

'Be it wind, be it wet, be it hail, be it sleet,
    Our ship must sail the foam;
The king's daughter to Noroway,
    'Tis we must take her home.'

They hoisted their sails on a Monday morn,
    With all the speed they may;
And they have landed in Noroway,
    Upon a Wednèsday.

They had not been in Noroway,
    But two weeks and a day,
When that the lords of Noroway,
    Began aloud to say,

'Ye Scottishmen spend all our king's gold,
    And all our queen's supply!'
'You lie, you lie, you liars loud,
    Full loud I hear you lie;

'For I brought as much white money
    As keeps my men and me,
And I brought a half-bushel of good red gold
    Out o'er the sea with me.

'Make ready, make ready, my merry men all!
    Our good ship sails the morn.'
'Now ever alack, my master dear,
    I fear a deadly storm!

'I saw the new moon late yestreen
    With the old moon in her arm;
And if we go to sea, master,
    I fear we'll come to harm.'

They had not sailed a league, a league,
    A league but barely three,
When the sky grew dark, and the wind blew loud,
    And gurly grew the sea.

The anchors snapped, the topmast cracked,
    It was such a deadly storm;
And the waves came over the broken ship,
    Till all her sides were torn.

'O where will I get a good sailor,
    To take my helm in hand,
Till I get up to the tall topmast
    To see can I spy land?'

'O here am I, a sailor good,
    To take the helm in hand,
Till you go up to the tall topmast.
    But I fear you'll ne'er spy land.'

He had not gone a step, a step,
   A step but barely one,
When a bolt flew out of the good ship's side,
   And the salt sea it came in.

'Go, fetch a web of the silken cloth,
   Another of the twine,
And wrap them into the good ship's side,
   And let not the sea come in.'

They fetched a web of the silken cloth,
   Another of the twine,
And they wrapped them into the good ship's sides,
   But still the sea came in.

O loth, loth were our good Scots lords
   To wet their cork-heeled shoon,
But long ere all the play was played,
   They wet their hats aboon.

And many was the feather bed
   That floated on the foam,
And many was the good lord's son
   That never more came home.

O long, long may the ladies sit,
   With their fans into their hand,
Before they see Sir Patrick Spens
   Come sailing to the strand!

And long, long may the maidens sit,
   With their gold combs in their hair,
A-waiting for their own dear loves!
   For them they'll see no mair.

Half-o'er, half-o'er to Aberdour,
   'Tis fifty fathoms deep;
And there lies good Sir Patrick Spens,
   With the Scots lords at his feet.

Thomas the Rhymer

True Thomas lay on Huntlie bank,
  A marvel with his eye spied he,
There he saw a lady bright
  Come riding down by the Eildon Tree.

Her skirt was of the grass-green silk,
  Her mantle of the velvet fine;
At each tuft of her horse's mane
  Hung fifty silver bells and nine.

True Thomas he pulled off his cap,
  And bowed him low down on his knee:
'Hail to thee, Mary, Queen of Heaven,
  For thy peer on earth could never be.'

5

'O no, O no, Thomas,' she said,
   'That name does not belong to me;
I'm but the Queen of fair Elfland,
   That am hither come to visit thee.

'Harp and carp, Thomas,' she said,
   'Harp and carp along with me;
And if you dare to kiss my lips,
   Sure of you, Thomas, I shall be.'

'Betide me weal, betide me woe,
   That doom shall never frighten me.'
Soon he has kissed her rosy lips,
   All underneath the Eildon Tree.

'Now you must go with me,' she said,
   'True Thomas, you must go with me;
And you must serve me seven years,
   Through weal or woe as may chance to be.'

She's mounted on her milk-white steed,
   She's ta'en true Thomas up behind;
And aye whene'er her bridle rang,
   The steed went swifter than the wind.

O they rode on, and farther on,
   The steed went swifter than the wind,
Until they reached a desert wide,
   And living land was left behind.

'Light down, light down, now, true Thomas,
   And lean your head upon my knee;
Abide ye there a little space,
   And I will show you marvels three.

'O see ye not yon narrow road,
   So thick beset with thorns and briars?
That is the Path of Righteousness,
   Though after it but few inquires.

'And see ye not yon broad, broad road,
  That lies across the lily leven?
That is the Path of Wickedness,
  Though some do call it the Road to Heaven.

'And see ye not yon bonny road,
  That winds about the ferny brae?
That is the Road to fair Elfland,
  And you and I must go that way.

'But, Thomas, you must hold your tongue,
  Whatever you may hear or see;
For speak ye word in Elfin-land,
  Ye'll ne'er win back to your own countrỳ.'

O they rode on and farther on,
  And they waded through rivers above the knee;
And they saw neither sun nor moon,
  But they heard the roaring of the sea.

At last they came to a garden green,
  And she plucked an apple that grew thereby:
'Take this for thy wages, Thomas,' she said,
  'It will give thee a tongue that can never lie.'

'My tongue is my own!' true Thomas he said,
  'A goodly gift you would give to me!
I could neither buy nor sell,
  At fair or mart where I might be.

'I could neither speak to prince or peer,
  Nor ask of grace from fair ladỳ!'
'Now hold thy peace, Thomas,' she said,
  'For as I say, so must it be.'

He has gotten a coat of the smooth, smooth cloth,
  And a pair of shoes of the velvet green;
And till seven years were gone and past,
  True Thomas on earth was never seen.

Willie Mackintosh

'Turn, Willie Mackintosh,
  Turn, I bid you;
If you burn Auchindown,
  Huntly will head you.'

'Head me or hang me,
  That cannot quail me:
I'll burn Auchindown
  Ere the life fail me.'

Coming down Deeside,
  In a clear morning,
Auchindown was in flame
  Ere the cock-crowing.

But coming o'er Cairn Croom,
  And looking down, man,
I saw Willie Mackintosh
  Burn Auchindown, man.

'Bonny Willie Mackintosh,
  Where left ye your men?'
'I left them in the Stapler—
  They'll not come home again.'

'Bonny Willie Mackintosh,
  Where have they gone?'
'I left them in the Stapler,
  Sleeping in their shoon.'

Erlington

Erlington had a fair daughter,
   I wot he did her a great sin;
For he has built a comely bower,
   And all to put that lady in.

And he has warned her sisters six,
   And so has he her brothers seven,
Either to watch her all the night,
   Or else to seek her morn and even.

She had not been in that comely bower,
   No not a night but barely one,
Till there was Willie, her own true dear love,
   Knocked at the door, crying 'Peace within!'

'O who is this at my bower door,
   That knocks so late, nor knows the gin?'
'O it is Willie, your own true dear love,
   I pray you rise and let me in.'

'For all so well as I like you, Willie,
   For all so well as I know the gin,
I would not for ten thousand pounds, love,
   No, not this night would I let you in.

'But in the green-wood is a glade, love,
   And in that glade there is a stone,
And there I'll come as soon the morn, love,
   No not a mile but barely one.

'I'll wear a glove on my right hand, love,
   And on my left hand I'll wear none;
I'll have with me my sisters six, love,
   And we will walk the woods our lone.'

Then she's gone to her bed again,
  Where she has lain till the cock crew thrice,
And then she said to her six sisters,
  'Maidens, 'tis time for us to rise.'

She put on her back her silken gown,
  And on her breast a silver pin,
And she's ta'en her sisters by the hand,
  All for to walk the green-wood in.

They had not walked in the bonny green-wood,
  No not an hour but barely one,
Till up start Willie, her own true dear love,
  Walking there in the wood his lone.

And he has kissed her sisters six,
  And he has sent them safely home,
But he has kept his own true dear love,
  Saying, 'We'll walk the woods our lone.

They had not walked in the bonny green-wood,
  No not an hour but barely one,
Till up start fifteen of the bravest outlaws
  That ever bore either flesh or bone.

Then up bespoke the foremost knight,
  And O but he spake angrily;
Says, 'Yield to me thy lady bright,
  This night shall walk the woods with me.'

'I like her well, my lady bright,
  And O, but my life it lies me near!
But before I lose my lady bright
  I'd rather lose my life so dear.'

But up and spoke the second knight,
  I wot he spake right boisterously,
Says, 'Yield me your life, and your lady bright
  This night shall walk the woods with me.'

'My lady is my life's reward,
  My life I will not yield to none;
But if ye be men of your manhood,
  You'll only fight me one by one.

'O sit you down, my dearest dear love,
  Sit down and hold my milk-white steed,
And see you do not change your cheer, love,
  Until you see my body bleed.'

He set his back unto an oak,
  He set his foot against a stone,
He's fighting all those fifteen outlaws,
  And killed them all but barely one.

And he has gone to his lady dear,
  And given her kisses many a one,
'Thou art my own, I have bought thee dear, love,
  And now we will walk the woods our lone.'

The Little Wee Man

As I was walking mine alone,
  Between a water and a wall,
There I spied a little wee man,
  And wow, but that wee man was small!

His legs were but a finger long,
  And thick and nimble was his knee;
Between his brows there was a span,
  And between his shoulders there was three.

He lifted a stone six feet in height,
  He lifted it up to his right knee,
And fifty yards and more I'm sure,
  I wot he made that stone to flee.

12

O little wee man, but you have power,
  And O, where may your dwelling be?'
'I dwell beneath yon bonny bower,
  O will you go with me and see?'

So on we leaped, and away we rode,
  Till we came to a little hall,
The roof was of the beaten gold,
  And the floor was of the crystal all.

There were pipers piping in every nook,
  And neat wee ladies dancing bonny;
And aye they danced and aye they sang,
  'He's been long away has our wee mannie.'

Out went the lights, down came the mist,
  Ladies nor mannie more could I see;
I turned about, and gave a look,
  Just at the foot of Benachie.

Young Bekie

Young Bekie was as brave a knight
  As ever sailed the sea,
And he's away to the court of France
  To serve for meat and fee.

He had not been in the court of France
  A twelvemonth nor so long,
Till he fell in love with the king's daughter
  And was thrown into prison strong.

The king he had but one daughter,
  Burd Isbel, fair and bright,
And she has to the prison house gone,
  Where sighing lay the knight.

'O if a lady would ransom me,
    At her stirrup-foot would I run;
Or if a widow would ransom me,
    I would swear to be her son.

'And if a maiden would ransom me,
    I would wed her with a ring,
I'd give her halls, I'd give her bowers,
    The bonny towers of Linne.'

O barefoot, barefoot went she out,
    And barefoot came she in,
It was not for want of hose and shoes,
    Nor time to put them on;

But all for fear that her father dear
    Would hear her making din;
She's stolen the keys of the prison house,
    To the prisoner she's gone in.

O when she saw him, young Bekie,
    Her heart was wondrous sore,
For the mice but and the bold rattens
    Had eaten his yellow hair.

She's given him a shaver for his beard,
    A comber for his hair;
Five hundred pounds in his pockèt,
    To spend and not to spare.

She's given him a steed was good at need,
    And a saddle of royal bone,
A leash of hounds of one litter,
    And Hector callèd one.

Between these two a vow was made,
    'Twas made full solemnly,
That ere three years were come and gone
    Well married they should be.

He had not been in his own country,
  A twelvemonth to an end,
Till he's forced to marry a duke's daughter,
  Or else to lose his land.

'Ohone, alas!' says young Bekie,
  'What shall I do?' says he;
'For I cannot win to Burd Isbel,
  And she knows not to come to me.

O it fell out upon a day
  Burd Isbel fell asleep,
And up it starts the Billy Blind,
  And stood at her bed-feet.

15

'O waken, waken, Burd Isbel,
   How can you sleep so long,
When this is Bekie's wedding day,
   And the marriage going on?

'You'll get you to your mother's bower,
   Think neither shame nor wrong,
And you'll take two of your mother's maids,
   To go with you along.

'You'll dress yourself in the red scarlèt,
   And your maids in dainty green,
And you'll put girdles about your middles
   Would buy an earl's demesne.

'O you'll go down by yon sea-side,
   And down by yon sea-strand;
So bonny will the Holland's boats
   Come rowing to your hand.

'You'll set your milk-white foot aboard,
   Cry, "Hail ye, Domine!"
And I shall be the steerer o't,
   To row you o'er the sea.'

She's hied her to her mother's bower,
   Thought neither shame nor wrong,
And she's taken two of her mother's maids,
   To go with her along.

She's dressed herself in the red scarlèt,
   And her maids in dainty green,
And they put girdles about their middles
   Would buy an earl's demesne.

And they went down by yon sea-side,
   And down by yon sea-strand;
So bonny did the Holland's boats
   Come rowing to their hand.

She set her milk-white foot aboard,
  Cried, "Hail ye, Domine!"
And the Billy Blind was the steerer o't,
  To row her o'er the sea.

When she came to young Bekie's gate,
  She heard the music play;
So well she knew from all she heard,
  It was his wedding day.

She's put her hand into her pocket,
  Given the porter guineas three;
'O take you that, you proud porter,
  Bid the bride-groom speak to me.'

O when that he came up the stair,
  He fell low on his knee;
He hailed the king, he hailed the queen,
  And he hailed him, young Bekie.

'O I've been porter at your gates
  This thirty years and three,
But there's three ladies at them now,
  Their like I ne'er did see.

'There's one of them dressed in red scarlèt,
  And two in dainty green,
And they have girdles about their middles
  Would buy an earl's demesne.'

Then out it spake the stately bride,
  Was all gold to the chin:
'If she be brave without,' she says,
  'We be as brave within.'

Then up it starts him, young Bekie,
  And the tears were in his e'e:
'I'll lay my life it's Burd Isbel,
  Come o'er the sea to me!'

O quickly ran he down the stair,
    Of fifteen made but three;
He's taken his bonny love in his arms,
    And kissed her tenderly.

'O have you forgotten, young Bekie,
    The vow you made to me,
When I took you out of prison strong,
    And gave you liberty?

'I gave you a steed was good at need,
    And a saddle of royal bone;
A leash of hounds of one litter,
    And Hector callèd one.'

It was well known what the lady said,
    That never a lie spake she;
For at every word the lady spake,
    The hound fell at her knee.

'Take home, take home your daughter dear,
    And my blessing with her take!
For I must marry my Burd Isbel,
    Come hither for my sake.'

'Is this the custom of your house,
    Or a fashion you think right,
To marry a maid in a May morning,
    And send her back at night?'

The Great Silkie of Sule Skerrie

An earthly nurse she sits and sings,
    And aye she sings, 'Ba, lily wean!
Little I know the babe's father,
    Far less the land that he dwells in.'

Then one arose at her bed-foot,
  And a grumly guest I'm sure was he:
'Here am I, the babe's father,
  Although I be not comèlỳ.

'I am a man upon the land,
  And I am a silkie in the sea,
And when I'm far and far from land
  My dwelling is in Sule Skerrie.'

Now he has taken a purse of gold,
  And he has put it upon her knee,
Saying, 'Give to me my little young son,
  And take thee up thy nurse's fee.

'And it shall pass on a summer's day,
  When the sun shines hot on every stone,
That I will take my little young son,
  And teach him for to swim alone.

'And thou shalt marry a proud gunner,
  And a proud gunner I'm sure he'll be;
And the very first shot that ever he shoots,
  He'll shoot both my young son and me.'

As I was a-walking mine alone,
   It was by the dawning of the day,
I heard two brothers making their moan,
   And I listened well what they did say.

The youngest to the eldest said,
   'Can we be merry, you and I?
There were three brothers of us born,
   And one of us is condemned to die.'

'An you would be merry, an you would be sad,
   What better would billie Archie be?
Unless I had thirty men to myself,
   And all to ride in my companỳ:

'Ten to hold the horses' heads,
   And other ten the watch to be,
And ten to break up the strong prison
   Where lies Archie, our own billìe!

'Had I but thirty sturdy men,
   Thirty of the best in Christiantìe,
I would go on to fair Dumfries,
   I would loose my brother and set him free.'

Then up and spake him mettled John Hall,
   (From lower Liddesdale came he):
'If I had eleven men to myself,
   It's aye the twelfth man I would be.'

Then up bespake him coarse Cawfield,
   (I wot but little good worth was he):
'Thirty men is few enough,
   And all to ride in our companỳ.'

O there was horsing, horsing in haste,
  And cracking of whips out over the lea;
Until they came to the Murraywhat,
  And they lighted there right speedilỳ.

'A smith! a smith!' Dickie he cries,
  'A smith, a smith, right speedilỳ,
To turn back the nails of our horses' shoes,
  For it's unknownsome we would be.'

'There lives a smith on the water-side,
  Will shoe my little black mare for me;
And I've a crown in my pockèt,
  And every groat for the smith shall be.'

'The night is murk, and it's very murk,
  And by candlelight I cannot well see;
The night is murk, and it's very pit murk,
  And there never will a nail go right for me.'

'Shame fall on you, smith, and your trade both,
  Cannot help a good fellow by your mysterỳ;
But commend me to thee, my little black mare,
  Thou'rt worth thy weight in gold to me!'

O there was horsing, horsing in haste,
  And cracking of whips out over the lea,
Until they came to the Bonshaw wood,
  Where they held their council privatelỳ.

Some says, 'We'll go the Annan road;
  'Tis the better road, we all agree.'
But up bespake then Dickie Hall,
  The wisest of that companỳ:

Says, 'Annan road is a public road,
  It's not the road that makes for me;
But we will through at Hoddam ford,
  It is the better road,' said he.

O there was horsing, horsing in haste,
　And cracking of whips out over the lea,
Until they came to Dumfries gate,
　And they lighted there right speedilỳ.

'There's five of us will hold the horse,
　And other five will watchmen be:
But who's the man among you all
　Will go to the prison door with me?'

O up then spake him mettled John Hall,
　(From lower Liddesdale came he),
'If it cost my life this very night,
　I'll go to the prison door with thee.'

'Be of good cheer, now, Archie lad!
　Be of good cheer, now, dear billìe!
Work thou within and we without,
　And the morn thou'lt dine at Cawfield with me!'

O Jockie Hall stepped to the door,
　And he bended low back on his knee,
And he made the bolts that the door hung on
　Leap from the wall right wantonlỳ.

He took the prisoner on his back,
　And down the prison stair came he;
The little black mare stood at the door,
　I wot a foot ne'er stirrèd she.

They laid the shackles out over her neck,
　And that was her gold twist to be;
And they came down through Dumfries town,
　And wow but they came speedilỳ!

The live-long night those twelve men rode,
　And aye till they were right wearỳ,
Until they came to the Murraywhat,
　And lighted there right speedilỳ.

'A smith! a smith!' Dickie Cawfield cries,
  'A smith, a smith, right speedilỳ,
To file the irons from my dear brother,
  For forward, forward we would be!'

They had not filed a shackle of iron,
  A shackle of iron but barely three,
When out and spake young Simon brave:
  'O do you not see what I do see?

'Lo! yonder comes Lieutenant Gordon,
  With a hundred men in his companỳ;
This night will be our lyke-wake night,
  The morn's the day we'll never see.'

O there was mounting, mounting in haste,
  And cracking of whips out over the lea;
Until they came to the Annan water,
  And it was flowing like the sea.

'My mare is young and very shy,
  And in the eddy she will drown me!'
'But you'll take mine, and I'll take thine,
  And soon through the water we shall be.'

Then up and spake him coarse Cawfield,
  (I wot but little good worth was he):
'We had better lose one than lose all the rest,
  We'll lose the prisoner, and we'll go free.'

'Shame fall on you and your lands both!
  Will you equal your lands to your born billìe?
But hey! bear up, my bonny black mare,
  And yet through the water we shall be!'

Now they did swim that wan water,
  And wow but they swam bonnilỳ!
Until they came to the other side,
  And they wrung their clothes right drunkilìe.

'Come through, come through, Lieutenant
    Gordon!
  Come through and drink some wine with me!
For there is an ale-house here hard by,
  And it shall not cost thee one pennỳ.'

'Throw me my irons,' quoth Lieutenant Gordon,
  'I wot they cost me dear enow.'
'The devil a bit,' quoth mettled John Hall,
  'They'll be good shackles for my plough.'

'Come through, come through, Lieutenant
    Gordon!
  Come through and drink some wine with me!
Yestreen I was your prisoner,
  But now this morning I am free.'

Binnorie

There were two sisters sat in a bower,
    Binnorie, O Binnorie;
There came a knight to be their wooer,
    By the bonnie mill-dams of Binnorie.

He courted the eldest with glove and ring,
    Binnorie, O Binnorie;
But he loved the youngest above all thing,
    By the bonnie mill-dams of Binnorie.

He courted the eldest with brooch and knife,
    Binnorie, O Binnorie;
But he loved the youngest above his life,
    By the bonnie mill-dams of Binnorie.

The eldest she was vexèd sore,
    Binnorie, O Binnorie;
And sore she envied her sister dear,
    By the bonnie mill-dams of Binnorie.

Upon a morning fair and clear,
    Binnorie, O Binnorie;
She cried upon her sister dear,
    By the bonnie mill-dams of Binnorie,

'O sister, come to yon river strand,'
    Binnorie, O Binnorie;
'And see our father's ships to land,'
    By the bonnie mill-dams of Binnorie.

She's ta'en her by the lily hand,
    Binnorie, O Binnorie,
And led her down to the river strand,
    By the bonnie mill-dams of Binnorie.

And as they walkèd by the linn,
  Binnorie, O Binnorie;
The eldest pushed the youngest in,
  By the bonnie mill-dams of Binnorie.

'O sister, sister, reach me your hand,'
  Binnorie, O Binnorie,
'And ye'll be heir to all my land,'
  By the bonnie mill-dams of Binnorie.

'Foul fail the hand that I would take,'
  Binnorie, O Binnorie;
'To rob me of my only mate,'
  By the bonnie mill-dams of Binnorie.

'O sister, sister, reach but your glove,'
  Binnorie, O Binnorie;
'And sweet William shall be your love,'
  By the bonnie mill-dams of Binnorie.

'Sink on, nor hope for hand or glove,'
  Binnorie, O Binnorie;
'And sweet William *shall* be my love,'
  By the bonnie mill-dams of Binnorie.

'Your cherry cheeks and yellow hair,'
  Binnorie, O Binnorie;
'Made me go maiden evermair,'
  By the bonnie mill-dams of Binnorie.

She clasped her hands about a broom root,
  Binnorie, O Binnorie;
But her cruel sister she loosed them out,
  By the bonnie mill-dams of Binnorie.

Sometimes she sank, sometimes she swam,
  Binnorie, O Binnorie;
Until she came to the miller's dam,
  By the bonnie mill-dams of Binnorie.

The miller's daughter was baking bread,
  Binnorie, O Binnorie;
She went for water as she had need,
  By the bonnie mill-dams of Binnorie.

'O father, father, draw your dam,'
  Binnorie, O Binnorie;
'There's either a mermaid or milk-white swan!'
  By the bonnie mill-dams of Binnorie.

The miller hasted and drew his dam,
  Binnorie, O Binnorie;
And there he found a drowned womàn,
  By the bonnie mill-dams of Binnorie.

You could not see her yellow hair,
  Binnorie, O Binnorie;
For the strings of pearls were twisted there,
  By the bonnie mill-dams of Binnorie.

You could not see her middle small,
  Binnorie, O Binnorie;
Her golden girdle was so broad,
  By the bonnie mill-dams of Binnorie.

You could not see her lily feet,
  Binnorie, O Binnorie;
Her golden fringes were so deep,
  By the bonnie mill-dams of Binnorie.

You could not see her fingers small,
  Binnorie, O Binnorie;
With diamond rings they were covered all,
  By the bonnie mill-dams of Binnorie.

And by there came a harper fine,
  Binnorie, O Binnorie;
Who harpèd when the king did dine,
  By the bonnie mill-dams of Binnorie.

And when he looked that lady on,
  Binnorie, O Binnorie;
He sighed and made a heavy moan,
  By the bonnie mill-dams of Binnorie.

He's made a harp of her breastbone,
  Binnorie, O Binnorie,
Whose sounds would melt a heart of stone,
  By the bonnie mill-dams of Binnorie.

He's taken three locks of her yellow hair,
  Binnorie, O Binnorie,
And with them strung his harp so rare,
  By the bonnie mill-dams of Binnorie.

He brought the harp to her father's hall,
  Binnorie, O Binnorie;
And there was the court assembled all,
  By the bonnie mill-dams of Binnorie.

He laid the harp upon a stone,
  Binnorie, O Binnorie;
And it began to play alone,
  By the bonnie mill-dams of Binnorie.

'O yonder sits my father the king,'
  Binnorie, O Binnorie;
And yonder sits my mother the queen,'
  By the bonnie mill-dams of Binnorie.

'And yonder stands my brother Hugh,'
  Binnorie, O Binnorie;
'And yonder my William, sweet and true,'
  By the bonnie mill-dams of Binnorie.

But the last tune that the harp played then,
  Binnorie, O Binnorie,
Was, 'Woe to my sister, false Ellèn!'
  By the bonnie mill-dams of Binnorie.

Young John

A fair maid sat in her bower-door,
  Wringing her lily hands,
And by it came a sprightly youth,
  Fast tripping o'er the strands.

'Where go ye, young John,' she says,
  'So early in the day?
It makes me think, by your fast trip,
  Your journey's far away.'

He turned about with a surly look,
  And said, 'What's that to thee?
I'm going to see a lovely maid,
  More fairer far than ye.'

'Now have you played me this, false love,
  In summer, 'mid the flowers?
I shall repay you back again,
  In winter, 'mid the showers.

'But again, dear love, and again, dear love,
  Will you not turn again?
For as you look to other women,
  Shall I to other men.'

'Go make your choice of whom you please,
  For I my choice will have;
I've chosen a maid more fair than thee,
  I never will deceive.'

She's kilted up her clothing fine,
  And after him went she;
But aye he said, 'You'll turn again,
  No farther go with me.'

'But again, dear love, and again, dear love,
    Will you ne'er love me again?
Alas, for loving you so well,
    And you not me again!'

The first town that they came to,
    He bought her brooch and ring;
And aye he bade her turn again,
    And no farther go with him.

'But again, dear love, and again, dear love,
    Will you ne'er love me again?
Alas, for loving you so well,
    And you not me again!'

The next town that they came to,
    He bought her muff and gloves;
But aye he bade her turn again,
    And choose some other loves.

'But again, dear love, and again, dear love,
    Will you ne'er love me again?
Alas, for loving you so well,
    And you not me again!'

The next town that they came to,
    His heart it grew more fain,
And he was as deep in love with her
    As she was o'er again.

The next town that they came to,
    He bought her a wedding gown,
And made her lady of halls and towers,
    Into sweet Berwick town.

Kemp Oweyne

Her mother died when she was young,
    Which gave her cause to make great moan;
Her father married the worst womàn
    That ever lived in Christendom.

She served that woman foot and hand,
    In every way she served could be;
Till wow that woman took her up
    And threw her over Craigy's sea.

Says, 'Lie you there, dove Isabel,
    And all my sorrows lie with thee;
Till Kemp Oweyne come o'er the sea,
    And ransom you with kisses three,
Let all the world do what they will,
    O! ransomed shall you never be.'

Her breath grew strong, her hair grew long,
    And twisted thrice about the tree;
And all the people far and near
    Thought that a savage beast was she.
This news did come to Kemp Oweyne,
    Where he dwelt o'er the sea.

Kemp Oweyne came o'er the sea,
    And on that savage beast looked he:
Her breath was strong, her hair was long,
    And twisted thrice about the tree;
And with a swing she came about,
    'Come to Craigy's sea, and kiss with me!

'Here is a royal belt,' she said,
   'That I have found in the green sea,
And while your body it is on,
   Drawn shall your blood never be;
But if you touch me, tail or fin,
   I swear my belt your death shall be.'

He steppèd in, gave her a kiss,
   The royal belt away brought he;
Her breath was strong, her hair was long,
   And twisted twice about the tree;
And with a swing she came about,
   'Come to Craigy's sea, and kiss with me!

'Here is a royal brand,' she said,
   'That I have found in the green sea;
And while your body it is on,
   Drawn shall your blood never be.
But if you touch me, tail or fin,
   I swear my brand your death shall be!'

He steppèd in, gave her a kiss,
   The royal brand away brought he;
Her breath was strong, her hair was long,
   And twisted once about the tree.
And with a swing she came about,
   'Come to Craigy's sea, and kiss with me!

'Here is a royal ring,' she said,
   'That I have found in the green sea;
And while your finger it is on,
   Drawn shall your blood never be.
But if you touch me, tail or fin,
   I swear my ring your death shall be!'

He steppèd in, gave her a kiss,
    The royal ring away brought he;
Her breath was sweet, her hair grew short,
    And twisted none about the tree;
And smilingly she came about,
    As fair a woman, as fair could be.

The Bonny Earl of Murray

Ye Highlands and ye Lowlands,
   O where have ye been?
They have slain the Earl of Murray,
   And have laid him on the green.

Now woe be to thee, Huntley!
   O what did I say?
I bade you bring him with you,
   But forbade you him to slay.

He was a brave gallant,
   And he rode at the ring;
And the bonny Earl of Murray,
   O he might have been a king!

He was a brave gallant,
   And he played at the ball;
And the bonny Earl of Murray
   Was the flower among them all!

He was a brave gallant,
   And he played at the glove,
And the bonny Earl of Murray,
   O he was the Queen's love!

O long will his Lady
   Look o'er the Castle Downe,
Ere she see the Earl of Murray
   Come sounding through the town!

The Wife of Usher's Well

There lived a wife at Usher's Well,
   And a wealthy wife was she;
She had three stout and stalwart sons,
   And sent them o'er the sea.

They had not been a week from her,
   A week but barely one,
When word came to that carline wife
   That her three sons were gone.

They had not been a week from her,
   A week but barely three,
When word came to that carline wife
   That her sons she'd never see.

'I wish the wind may never cease,
  Nor troubles in the flood,
Till my three sons come home to me
  In earthly flesh and blood!'

It fell about the Martinmas,
  When the nights are long and murk,
That the carline wife's three sons came home,
  And their hats were of the birk.

It neither grew in marsh nor ditch,
  Nor in trench anywhere,
But at the gates of Paradise
  That birk was growing fair.

'Blow up the fire, my maidens,
  Bring water from the well!
For all my house shall feast this night,
  Since my three sons are well.'

And she has made for them a bed,
  She's made it large and wide;
And she's taken her mantle her about,
  Sat down by the bedside.

Up then crew the red, red cock,
  And up and crew the grey;
The eldest to the youngest said,
  ' 'Tis time we were away.

'The cock doth crow, the day doth dawn,
  The channering worm doth chide;
If we be missed out of our place,
  A sore pain we must bide.'

'Lie still, lie still, but a little wee while,
  Lie still, if but we may;
If my mother should miss us when she wakes,
  She'll go mad ere it be day.

'Our mother has no more but us—
  See where she leans asleep,
The mantle that was about herself,
  She has wrapped it round our feet.'

O it's they have ta'en up their mother's mantle,
  And they've hung it on a pin:
'O long may you hang, my mother's mantle,
  Ere you wrap us again!'

'Fare you well, my mother dear,
  Farewell to barn and byre,
And fare you well, the bonny lass
  That kindles my mother's fire!'

Edward, Edward!

'Why does your brand so drop with blood,
        Edward, Edward?
Why does your brand so drop with blood,
  And why so sad go ye, O?'
'O I have killed my hawk so good,
        Mother, mother;
O I have killed my hawk so good,
  And I had no more but he, O.'

39

'Your hawk's blood was never so red,
  Edward, Edward;
Your hawk's blood was never so red,
  My dear son, I tell thee, O.'
'O I have killed my red-roan steed,
  Mother, mother;
O I have killed my red-roan steed,
  That went so fair and free, O.'

'Your steed was old, and ye have more,
  Edward, Edward;
Your steed was old, and you have more,
  Some other dole ye dree, O.'
'O I have killed my father dear,
  Mother, mother;
O I have killed my father dear,
  Alas, and woe is me, O!'

'And what penance will ye dree for that,
  Edward, Edward?
What penance will ye dree for that,
  My dear son, now tell me, O.'
'I'll set my foot in yonder boat,
  Mother, mother,
I'll set my foot in yonder boat,
  And I'll fare o'er the sea, O.'

'And what will ye do with your towers and your hall,
  Edward, Edward?
And what will ye do with your towers and your hall,
  That were so fair to see, O?'
'I'll let them stand till down they fall,
  Mother, mother;
I'll let them stand till down they fall,
  For here never more must I be, O.'

'And what will ye leave to your bairns and your wife,
  Edward, Edward?
And what will ye leave to your bairns and your wife,

When ye go o'er the sea, O?'
'The world's room: let them beg through life,
        Mother, mother;
The world's room: let them beg through life,
  For them never more will I see, O.'

'And what will you leave to your own mother dear,
        Edward, Edward?
And what will ye leave to your own mother dear,
  My dear son, now tell me, O?'
'The curse of hell from me shall ye bear,
        Mother, mother;
The curse of hell from me shall ye bear,
  Such counsels ye gave to me, O!'

The Birth of Robin Hood

O Willie's large of limb and bone,
  And come of high degree,
And he is gone to Earl Richard
  To serve for meat and fee.

Earl Richard had but one daughter,
  Fair as a lily-flower,
And they made up their love-contract,
  Like proper paramour.

It fell upon a summer's night,
  When the leaves were fair and green,
That Willie met his gay ladỳ,
  Into the wood unseen.

'O if my father should get word
  Of the love 'twixt you and me,
Before that he should eat or drink,
  He'd hang you from yon tree.

41

'But ye'll come to my bower, Willie,
    Just as the sun goes down,
And catch me in your arms two,
    And let me not fall down.'

O when the sun was now gone down,
    He's gone unto her bower,
And there by the low light of the moon,
    Her window she looked o'er.

Into a cloak of red scarlèt
    She's leaped, fearless of harm,
And Willie was large of limb and bone,
    And caught her in his arm.

And they've gone to the good green-wood,
    And ere the night was done,
All among the leaves so green,
    She's born him a bonny young son.

When night was gone, and day was come,
    And the sun began to peep,
It's up and rose then Earl Richard
    Out of his drowsy sleep.

He's called upon his merry young men,
    By one, by two, and by three;
'O what has come of my daughter dear
    That she's not come to me?'

'I dreamed a dreary dream last night,
    God grant it come to good!
I dreamed I saw my daughter dear
    Drown in the salt sea flood.

'But if my daughter be dead or sick,
    Or yet be stolen away,
I make a vow, and I'll keep it true,
    I'll hang you all this day!'

They sought her back, they sought her forth,
   They sought her up and down;
They got her in the good green-wood,
   Nursing her bonny young son.

He took the bonny boy in his arms,
   And kissed him tenderly̖;
Says, 'Though I would your father hang,
   Your mother's dear to me.'

He kissed him o'er and o'er again,
   'My grandson I thee claim,
And Robin Hood in good green-wood,
   It's that shall be your name.'

O many one sings of grass, of grass,
   And many one sings of corn;
And many one sings of Robin Hood,
   Knows not where he was born.

It was not in the hall, the hall,
   Nor in the painted bower,
But it was in the good green-wood,
   Among the lily-flower.

Robin Hood
and Alan a Dale

Come listen to me, you gallants so free,
  All you that love mirth for to hear,
And I will you tell of a bold outlàw,
  That lived in Nottinghamshire.

As Robin Hood in the forest stood,
  All under the green-wood tree,
There he was ware of a brave young man,
  As fine as fine might be.

The youngster was clothèd in scarlet red,
  In scarlet fine and gay,
And he did frisk it over the plain,
  And chanted a roundelay.

As Robin Hood next morning stood,
  Amongst the leaves so gay,
There he did espy the same young man
  Come drooping along the way.

The scarlet he wore the day before,
  It was clean cast away;
And every step he fetched a sigh,
  'Alack and a well a day!'

Then steppèd forth brave Little John,
  And Much the miller's son,
Which made the young man bend his bow,
  When he saw them come on.

'Stand off, stand off!' the young man said,
  'What is your will with me?'
'You must come before our master straight,
  Under yon green-wood tree.'

And when he came bold Robin before,
   Robin asked him courteouslỳ,
'O hast thou any money to spare,
   For my merry men and me?'

'I have no money,' the young man said,
   'But five shillings and a ring;
And that I have kept this seven long years,
   To have it at my weddìng.

'Yesterday I should have married a maid,
   But she is now from me ta'en,
And chosen to be an old knight's delight,
   Whereby my poor heart is slain.'

'What is thy name?' then said Robin Hood,
   'Come tell me, without any fail.'
'By the faith of my body,' then said the young man,
   'My name it is Alan a Dale.'

'What wilt thou give me,' said Robin Hood,
   'In ready gold or fee,
To help thee to thy true-love again,
   And deliver her unto thee?'

'I have no money,' then said the young man,
   'Nor ready gold nor fee,
But I will swear upon a book
   Thy true servant for to be.'

'But how many miles to thy true-love?
   Come tell me without any guile.'
'By the faith of my body,' then said the young man,
   'It is but five little mile.'

Then Robin he hasted over the plain,
   Did neither stop nor stay,
Until he came unto the church,
   Where the wedding should be that day.

'What dost thou here?' the Bishop he said,
  'I prithee now tell to me.'
'I am a bold harper,' quoth Robin Hood,
  'And the best in the north countrỳ.'

'O welcome, O welcome,' the Bishop he said,
  'That music best pleaseth me.'
'You shall have no music,' quoth Robin Hood,
  'Till the bride and the bridegroom I see.'

With that came in a wealthy knight,
  Which was both grave and old,
And after him a finikin lass,
  Did shine like glistering gold.

'This is no fit match,' quoth bold Robin Hood,
  'That you do seem to make here;
For since we are come unto the church,
  The bride she shall choose her own dear.'

Then Robin Hood put his horn to his mouth,
  And blew blasts two or three;
When four and twenty bowmen bold
  Came leaping over the lea.

And when they came into the churchyard,
  Marching all in a row,
The first man was Alan a Dale,
  To give bold Robin his bow.

'This is thy true-love,' Robin he said,
  'Young Alan, as I hear say;
And you shall be married at this same time,
  Before we depart away.'

'That shall not be,' the Bishop he said,
  'For thy word it shall not stand;
They shall be three times asked in church,
  As the law is of our land.'

Robin Hood pulled off the Bishop's coat,
    And put it on Little John;
'By the faith of my body,' then Robin said,
    'This cloth doth make thee a man!'

When Little John went into the quire,
    The people began for to laugh;
He asked them seven times in the church,
    Lest three should not be enough.

'Who gives me this maid?' then said Little John,
    Quoth Robin, 'That do I!
And he that doth take her from Alan a Dale
    Full dearly he shall her buy.'

And thus having ended this merry wedding,
    The bride looked as fresh as a queen;
And so they returned to the merry green-wood,
    Amongst the leaves so green.

But how many moons be in the year?
  There are thirteen I say:
The midsummer moon is the merriest of all,
  Next to the merry moon of May.

In summer time, when leaves grow green,
  And flowers are fresh and gay,
Robin Hood and his merry men,
  They were disposed to play.

Then some would leap, and some would run,
  And some use artillerỳ;
'Which of you can a good bow draw,
  A good archer to be?

'Which of you can kill a buck,
  Or who a doe can slay?
Or who can kill a hart of grease,
  Five hundred feet away?'

Will Scathèlock he killed a buck,
  And Much a doe did slay,
And Little John killed a hart of grease,
  Five hundred feet away.

'God's blessing on thy heart,' said Robin,
  'That hath shot such a shot for me;
I would ride my horse an hundred miles,
  To find one could match with thee!'

That caused Will Scathèlock to laugh,
  He laughed full heartilỳ;
'There's a curtal friar in Fountains Abbey,
  Will beat both him and thee.

'That curtal friar in Fountains Abbey,
  Can well draw a long bow,
He will beat you and your yeomèn,
  Set them all in a row.'

Robin Hood took a solemn oath,
 It was by Mary free,
That he would neither eat nor drink
 Till that friar he did see.

Robin put on his harness good,
 On his head a cap of steel,
Broad sword and buckler by his side,
 And they became him well.

He took his bow into his hand,
 It was made of trusty tree;
With a sheaf of arrows at his belt,
 To Fountains Dale went he.

And coming unto Fountains Dale,
 No farther would he ride,
There he was ware of a curtal friar,
 Walked by the water-side.

The friar had on a harness good,
 On his head a cap of steel,
Broad sword and buckler by his side,
 And they became him well.

Robin lighted off his horse,
 And tied him to a thorn;
'Carry me over the water, thou curtal friar,
 Or else thy life's forlorn.'

The friar took Robin Hood on his back,
 Deep water he did bestride,
And he spake neither good word nor bad,
 Till he came at the other side.

Lightly leaped Robin off the friar's back;
 The friar said to him again,
'Carry me over this water, my fine fellòw,
 Or it shall breed thy pain.'

Robin Hood took the friar on his back,
    Deep water he did bestride,
And he spake neither good word nor bad,
    Till he came at the other side.

Lightly leaped the friar off Robin Hood's back;
    Robin said to him again,
'Carry me over this water, thou curtal friar,
    Or it shall breed thy pain.'

The friar took Robin Hood on his back,
    And steppèd up to the knee:
Till he came at the middle stream,
    Neither good nor bad spake he.

And coming to the middle stream,
    There he threw Robin in:
'And choose thee, choose thee, my fine fellòw,
    Whether thou'lt sink or swim!'

Robin Hood swam to a bush of broom,
    The friar to a wicker wand;
Bold Robin Hood is gone to shore,
    And took his bow in his hand.

One of his best arrows under his belt
    To the friar he let fly;
The curtal friar with his steel buckler
    He put that arrow by.

'Shoot on, shoot on, thou fine fellòw,
    Shoot on as thou hast begun;
If thou shoot here a summer's day,
    Thy mark I will not shun.'

Robin Hood shot passing well,
    Till his arrows all were gone;
They took their swords and steel bucklers,
    And fiercely they fought on.

They fought from ten of the clock that day,
   Till four in the afternoon;
Then Robin Hood came to his knees,
   Of the friar to beg a boon.

'A boon, a boon, thou curtal friar!
   I beg it on my knee;
Give me leave to set my horn to my mouth,
   And to blow blasts three.'

'That will I do,' said the curtal friar,
  'Of thy blasts I have no doubt;
I hope thou'lt blow so passing well,
  Till both thy eyes fall out!'

Robin Hood set his horn to his mouth,
  He blew but blasts three:
Half a hundred yeomen, with bows bent,
  Came raking over the lea.

'Whose men are these?' then said the friar,
  'That come so hastilỳ?'
'These men are mine,' said Robin Hood;
  'Friar, what is that to thee?'

'A boon, a boon,' said the curtal friar,
  'The like I gave to thee!
Give me leave to set my fist to my mouth,
  And to whistle whistles three.'

'That will I do,' said Robin Hood,
  'Or else I were to blame;
Three whistles in a friar's fist
  Would make me glad and fain.'

The friar he set his fist to his mouth,
  And whistled whistles three;
Half a hundred good ban-dogs
  Came leaping over the lea.

'Here's for every man of thine a dog,
  And I myself for thee!'
'Nay, by my faith,' said Robin Hood,
  'Friar, that may not be!'

Two dogs at once to Robin did go,
  One behind, the other before;
Robin Hood's mantle of Lincoln green
  Off from his back they tore.

And whether his men shot east or west,
   Or shot they north or south,
The curtal dogs, so taught they were,
   Caught the arrows in their mouth.

'Take up thy dogs,' said Little John,
   'Friar, at my bidding be!'
'Whose man art thou,' said the curtal friar,
   'Comes here to prate with me?'

'I am Little John, Robin Hood's man,
   Friar, I will not lie;
If thou take not thy dogs up soon,
   Then take them up will I.'

Little John had a bow in his hand,
   He shot with might and main;
Soon half a score of the friar's dogs
   Lay dead upon the plain.

'Hold thy hand, good fellow,' said the curtal friar,
   'Thy master and I will agree;
And we will have new orders taken,
   With all the haste may be.'

'If thou wilt forsake fair Fountains Dale,
   And Fountains Abbey free,
Every Sunday throughout the year,
   A noble shall be thy fee.

'And every holy day throughout the year,
   Changed shall thy garment be,
If thou wilt go to merry Sherwood,
   And there remain with me.'

This curtal friar had kept Fountains Dale,
   Seven long years or more;
There was neither knight, lord, nor earl
   Could make him yield before.

In summer when the woods be bright,
   And leaves be large and long,
It is merry walking in the fair forèst
   To hear the small birds' song.

To see the deer draw to the dale,
   And leave the hills so high,
And shadow them in good green-wood,
   Under green leaves to lie.

'Now by my faith,' said Robin Hood,
   'A dream I had this night,
I dreamed me of two bold yeomèn,
   That fast with me did fight.

'Methought they did me beat and bind,
   And took from me my bow.
If I be Robin alive in this land,
   I'll get even with those two.'

'Dreams are swift, master,' said Little John,
   'As the wind that blows o'er a hill;
For if it be never so loud this night,
   Tomorrow it may be still.'

'Dress ye, make ready, my merry men all,
   And John shall go with me,
For I'll go seek yon bold yeomèn
   In green-wood where they be.'

They cast on them their gowns of green,
   And their bows they took each one,
And all away to the good green-wood,
   A shooting forth are gone.

And when they came to the merry green-wood,
   Where they had gladdest be;
There were they ware of a bold yeomàn,
   His body leaned to a tree.

A sword and dagger he wore by his side,
   Of many a man the bane;
And he was clad in a horse's hide,
   Top and tail and mane.

'Stand you still, Master,' said Little John,
    'Under this trusty tree,
And I will go to yon bold yeomàn,
    To know his meaning trulỳ.'

'Ah John! By me thou settest no store,
    And that is strange to find!
How oft send I my men before,
    And tarry myself behind?

'It is no cunning a knave to know,
    If a man but hear him speak;
Were it not for bursting of my bow,
    Thy head, John, would I break!'

As it is often words breed bale,
    So they parted Robin and John;
And John is gone to Barnèsdale,
    The paths he knew each one.

But when he came to Barnèsdale,
    Great heaviness there he had,
For there he found two of his own comràdes,
    Were slain both in a glade.

And Scarlet a-foot he flying was
    Fast over stock and stone,
For the Sheriff and with him seven score men
    Fast after him is gone.

'Yet one shoot will I shoot,' quoth John,
    'By Christ His might and main;
I make that fellow that flies so fast,
    To stop he shall be fain.'

Then John bent up his good yew-bow
    And got him ready to shoot;
The bow was made of a tender bough,
    And fell down to his foot.

'Woe worth thee, wicked wood!' said John,
  'That e'er thou grew on a tree!
For now this day thou art my bale,
  My boot when thou should be.'

His shot it was but loosely shot,
  Yet it flew not in vain,
For it met one of the Sheriff's men,
  Good William à Trent was slain.

It had been better for William à Trent
  To have been hangèd upon a gallòw,
Than to be that day in merry green-wood
  To meet Little John's arròw.

But as it be said, when men be met,
  Five can do more than three,
The Sheriff hath taken Little John,
  And bound him fast to a tree.

'Thou shalt be drawn by dale and down,
  And hangèd high on a hill.'
'But thou mayst fail,' said Little John,
  'If it be Christ His will.'

Let us leave talking of Little John,
  And think of Robin Hood,
How he is gone to the bold yeoman,
  Where under the leaves he stood.

'Good morrow, good fellow,' said Robin so fair,
  'Good morrow, good fellow,' said he.
'Methinks by this bow thou bears in thy hand,
  A good archer thou shouldst be.'

'I am strayed from my way,' said the archer then,
  'Am lost in the wood so wide.'
'I'll lead thee through the wood,' said Robin,
  'Good fellow, I'll be thy guide.'

'I seek an outlaw,' the stranger said,
　'Called Robin Hood so bold.
Rather I'd meet with that proud outlaw
　Than forty pounds of gold.'

'If you two met it would be seen
　Which were the better man;
But let us under the leaves so green
　Some other pastime plan.

'Let us make some trials of skill
　Among the woods so green;
We yet may meet with Robin Hood
　At a time we do not dream.'

They cut them down two summer shrubs
　That grew both under a thorn,
And set them three score roods apart
　To shoot the marks in turn.

'Lead on, good fellow,' quoth Robin Hood,
　'Lead on, I do bid thee.'
'Nay, by my faith, good fellow,' he said,
　'My leader thou shalt be.'

The first good shot that Robin led,
　He missed by an inch, no more;
The yeoman he was an archer good,
　But he missed by half a score.

The second shot had the bold yeomàn,
　He shot within the garlànd:
But Robin he shot far better than he,
　For he cleft in two the wand.

'God's blessing upon thy heart!' he said,
　'Good fellow, thy shooting is good;
For if thy heart be as good as thy hand,
　Thou wert better than Robin Hood.

'Now tell me thy name, good fellow,' he said
   'Under the leaves of lime.'
'Nay, by my faith,' quoth good Robin,
   'Till thou hast told me thine.'

'I dwell by dale and down,' quoth he,
   'And Robin to take I'm sworn;
And when I am called by my right name,
   I am Guy of good Gisbòrne.'

'My dwelling is in this wood,' says Robin,
   'By thee I set right nought:
I am Robin Hood of Barnèsdale,
   Whom thou so long has sought.'

He that had been neither kith nor kin,
   Might have seen a full fair sight,
To see how together these yeomen went,
   With blades both brown and bright:

To see how these yeomen together they fought
   Two hours of a summer's day:
Yet neither Sir Guy nor Robin Hood,
   Made ready to flee away.

Robin was careless of a root,
   And stumbled at that tide;
And Guy was quick and nimble withal,
   And hit him o'er the left side.

'Ah, dear Lady!' said Robin Hood,
   'Of mother and maids the flower,
I think it was never man's destiny,
   To die before his hour!'

Robin thought on Our Lady dear,
   And soon leaped up again,
And straight he came with a back-handed stroke,
   And he Sir Guy hath slain.

Says, 'Lie there, lie there, good Sir Guy,
    And with me be not wroth;
If thou hadst the worse strokes at my hand,
    Thou shalt have the better cloth.'

Robin took off his gown of green,
    And on Sir Guy it did throw,
And he put on that horse's hide,
    That clad him top to toe.

'The bow, the arrows, and little horn,
    Now with me I will bear;
For I will away to Barnèsdale,
    To see how my men do fare.'

Robin set Sir Guy's horn to his mouth,
    A loud blast in it did blow;
'Twas heard by the Sheriff of Nottingham,
    As he leaned under a bough.

'Hearken! hearken!' then said the Sheriff,
    'I hear now tidings good,
For yonder I hear Sir Guy's horn blow,
    And he hath slain Robin Hood.

'Yonder I hear Sir Guy's horn blow,
    It blows so well at this tide;
And yonder comes that bold yeoman,
    Clad in his horse's hide.

'Come hither, come hither, thou good Sir Guy,
    Ask what thou wilt of me.'
'O I will have none of thy gold,' said Robin,
    'Nor I will none of thy fee.

'But now I have slain the master,' he says,
    'Let me go strike the knave;
This is all the reward I ask,
    And none other will I have.'

'Thou art a madman,' then said the Sheriff,
  'Thou shouldst have had a knight's fee;
But seeing thy asking has been so bad,
  Well granted it shall be.'

When Little John heard his master speak,
  Well knew he 'twas Robin Hood,
'Now loosed I shall be,' quoth Little John,
  'If Christ to us be good.'

Robin he hied him to Little John,
  He thought to loose him in haste,
But the Sheriff and all his company
  Came after him full fast.

'Stand aback! Stand aback!' said Robin Hood,
  'Why draw ye me so near?
It was never the custom in our country,
  One's shrift another should hear.'

Then Robin pulled forth an Irish knife,
  And loosed John hand and foot,
And gave him Sir Guy's bow into his hand,
  And bade it be his boot.

Then John took Sir Guy's bow in his hand,
  His bolts and arrows each one;
When the Sheriff saw Little John bend his bow,
  He thought it was time to be gone.

Towards his house in Nottingham town,
  He fled full fast away;
And so did all his company;
  Not one behind would stay.

But he could neither go so fast,
  Nor away so fast could start,
But Little John with an arrow so broad,
  Did cleave in twain his heart.

Robin Hood and the Butcher

Come, all you brave gallants, and listen a while,
    That are in the bowers within,
For of Robin Hood, that archer so good,
    A song I intend for to sing.

Upon a time it chancèd so,
    That Robin in forest did spy
A jolly butchèr, with a bonny fine mare,
    With his flesh to the market did hie.

'Good morrow, good morrow,' said jolly Robìn,
    'What food hast? Tell unto me;
And thy trade to me tell, and where thou doest dwell,
    For I like well thy companỳ.'

The butcher he answered jolly Robìn,
    'No matter where I do dwell;
For a butcher I am, and to fair Nottinghàm
    I am going my flesh for to sell.'

'What price is thy flesh?' said jolly Robìn,
    'Come tell it soon unto me;
And the price of thy mare, be she never so dear,
    For a butcher fain would I be.'

'The price of my flesh,' the butcher replied,
    'I soon will tell unto thee;
With my bonny mare, and they are not dear,
    Four marks thou must give unto me.'

'Four marks I will give thee,' says jolly Robìn,
    'Four marks it shall be thy fee;
Thy money come count, and let me mount,
    For a butcher I fain would be.'

Now Robin he is to Nottingham gone,
  His butcher's trade for to begin,
With good intent, to the Sheriff he went,
  And there he took up his inn.

When other butchers they opened their meat,
  Bold Robin he then begun;
But how for to sell he knew not well,
  For a butcher he was but young.

When other butchers no meat could sell,
  Robin got gold and fee;
For he sold more meat for one penny
  Than the others could do for three.

But when he sold his meat so fast,
  No butcher could by him thrive;
For he sold more meat for one penny,
  Than others could do for five.

The butchers they steppèd to jolly Robìn,
  Acquainted with him for to be.
'Come, brother,' one said, 'we be all of one trade,
  Come, will you go dine with me?'

'Accursed of his heart,' said jolly Robìn,
  'That a butcher doth deny!
I will go with you, my brethren true,
  As fast as I can hie.'

But when to the Sheriff's house they came,
  To dinner they hied apace,
And Robin he the man must be
  Before them all to say grace.

'Pray God bless us all,' said jolly Robìn,
  'And our meat within this place;
A cup of sack good, to nourish our blood,
  And so I do end my grace.

'Come fill us more wine,' said jolly Robìn,
  'Let us drink and never give o'er;
For the shot I will pay, ere I go my way,
  If it cost me five pound and more.'

'This is a mad blade,' the butchers then said;
   Says the Sheriff, 'He's some prodigàl,
That his land has sold, for silver and gold,
   And meaneth to spend it all.

'Hast thou any horned beasts?' the Sheriff inquired,
   'Good fellow, to sell unto me?'
'Yea, a plenty I have, good Master Sheriff,
   I have hundreds two or three.

'And a hundred acre of good free land,
   An it please you go for to see;
And I'll make you as good assurance of it
   As ever my father made me.'

The Sheriff he saddled a good palfrỳ,
   With three hundred pound of gold,
And away he went with bold Robin Hood,
   His hornèd beasts to behold.

Away then the Sheriff and Robin did ride,
   To the forest of merry Sherwood;
Then the Sheriff did say, 'God bless us this day
   From a man they call Robin Hood!'

But then a little farther they came,
   Bold Robin he chanced for to spy
A hundred head of good red deer
   Come tripping the Sheriff full nigh.

'How like you my horned beasts, Master Sheriff?
   They be fat and fair for to see.'
'I tell thee, good fellow, I would I were gone,
   For I like not thy companỳ!'

Then Robin he set his horn to his mouth,
   And blew but blastès three;
Then quickly anon there came Little John,
   And all his companỳ

'What is your will?' then said Little John,
  'Good master, come tell it to me.'
'O the Sheriff of Nottingham here have I brought,
  This day to dine with thee.'

'He is welcome to me,' then said Little John,
  'I hope he will honestly pay;
I know he has gold, if it be but well told,
  Will serve us to drink a whole day.'

Robin Hood took his mantle from off his back,
  And laid it upon the ground;
And out of the Sheriff's portmanteau
  He took three hundred pound.

Then Robin he brought him out through the wood,
  Set him on his dapple gray;
'O have me commended, good sir, to your wife!'
  So Robin went laughing away.

Robin Hood and the Two Priests

I have heard talk of bold Robin Hood
  And of brave Little John,
Of Friar Tuck and Scathèlock,
  And Much, the miller's son.

But such a tale as this, before
  I think there never was none;
For Robin Hood disguised himself,
  And through the wood is gone.

Like to a friar bold Robin Hood
  Was dressed in his array;
With hood, gown, beads, and crucifix,
  He passed upon the way.

He had not gone miles two or three,
    But 'twas his chance to spy
Two lusty priests, clad all in black,
    Come riding gallantlỳ.

'Benedicite,' then said Robin Hood,
    'Some pity on me take;
Cross you my hand with a silver groat,
    For Our dear Lady's sake!

'For I have been wandering all this day.
    And nothing could I get;
Not so much as one poor cup of drink,
    Nor bit of bread to eat.'

'By my holydame,' the priests replied,
    'We never a penny have;
For we this morning have been robbed,
    And could no money save.'

'I am much afraid,' said Robin Hood,
    'That you both do tell a lie;
And now before that you go hence,
    I am resolved to try.'

When as the priests heard him say that,
    They rode away amain;
But Robin betook him to his heels,
    And soon caught them again.

Then Robin Hood laid hold of them both,
    And pulled them from their horse;
'O spare us, friar!' the priests cried out,
    'On us have some remorse!'

'You said you had no money,' quoth he;
    'Wherefore without delay
We three will fall down on our knees,
    And for money we will pray.'

The priests they could not him gainsay,
    But down they kneeled with speed;
'Send us, O send us,' then quoth they,
    'Some money to serve our need!'

The priests did pray with mournful cheer,
    Sometimes their hands did wring,
Sometimes they wept and cried aloud,
    Whilst Robin did merrily sing.

When they had prayed an hour's space,
    The priests did still lament;
Then quoth bold Robin, 'Now let's see
    What money heaven hath us sent.

'We will be sharers all alike
    Of the money that we have;
And there is never a one of us
    That his fellows shall deceive.'

The priests their hands in their pockets put,
    But money would find none;
'We'll search ourselves,' said Robin Hood,
    'Each other, one by one.'

Then Robin took pains to search them both,
    And found good store of gold;
Five hundred pieces presently
    Upon the grass was told.

'Here's a brave show,' said Robin Hood
    'Such store of gold to see!
And you shall each one have a part
    'Cause you prayed so heartily.'

He gave them fifty pounds a-piece,
    And the rest for himself did keep;
The priests they durst not speak one word,
    But they sighèd wondrous deep.

With that the priests rose up from their knees,
    And thought to have parted so;
'Nay, stay,' said Robin, 'one thing more
    I have to say ere you go.

'You shall be sworn,' said Robin Hood,
    'Upon this holy grass,
That you will never tell lies again,
    Which way soever you pass.

'The second oath you shall take, it is this,
    Be charitable to the poor;
Say you have met with a holy friar,
    And I desire no more.'

He set them upon their horses again,
    And away then did they ride;
And he returned to the merry green-wood,
    With great joy, mirth and pride.

Robin Hood
and the Widow's Three Sons

There are twelve months in all the year,
    As I hear many men say,
But the merriest month in all the year
    Is the merry month of May.

Now Robin is to Nottingham gone,
    With a link and a down and a day!
And there he met a silly old woman,
    Was weeping along the way.

'What news, what news, thou silly old woman?
    Now tell me without a lie.'
Said she, 'Three squires in Nottingham town
    Today is condemned to die.'

'O have they parishes burnt?' he said,
  'Or have they ministers slain?
Or have they robbed any virgin,
  Or other men's wives have ta'en?'

'They have no parishes burnt, good sir,
  Nor yet have ministers slain,
Nor have they robbed any virgin,
  Nor other men's wives have ta'en.'

'O what have they done?' said bold Robin Hood,
  'I pray thee tell to me.'
'It's all for slaying the King's fallow deer,
  Bearing their long bows with thee.'

71

Now Robin Hood is to Nottingham gone,
  With a link and a down and a day!
And there he met with a silly old palmer,
  Was walking along the highwày.

'What news, what news, thou silly old man?
  What news I do thee pray?'
Said he, 'Three squires in Nottingham town
  Are condemned to die this day.'

'Come change thy apparel with me, old man,
  Come change thy apparel for mine;
Here is forty shillings in good silver,
  Go drink it in beer or wine.'

'O thine apparel is good,' he said,
  'And mine is ragged and torn;
Wherever you go, wherever you ride,
  Laugh ne'er an old man to scorn.'

'Come change thy apparel with me, old churl,
  Come change thy apparel with mine;
Here are twenty pieces of good red gold,
  Go feast thy brethren with wine.'

Then he put on the old man's hat,
  It stood full high on the crown:
'The first bold bargain that I come at,
  It shall make thee come down!'

Then he put on the old man's cloak,
  Was patched black, blue, and red;
He thought no shame, all the day long,
  To wear the bags of bread.

Then he put on the old man's breeks,
  Was patched from front to side;
'By the truth of my body,' said bold Robin Hood,
  'This man loved little pride!'

Then he put on the old man's hose,
  Was patched from knee to wrist;
'By the truth of my body,' said bold Robin Hood,
  'I'd laugh if I had any list.'

Then he put on the old man's shoes,
  Was patched both beneath and aboon;
Then Robin Hood swore a solemn oath,
  'It's good habit that makes the man.'

Now Robin is to Nottingham gone,
  With a link and a down and a down!
And there he met with the proud Sheriff,
  Was walking along the town.

'O save, O save, O Sheriff,' he said,
  'O save, and may you see!
And what will you give to a silly old man,
  Today will your hangman be?'

'Some suits, some suits,' the Sheriff he said,
  'Some suits I'll give to thee;
Some suits, some suits, and pence thirteen
  Today is a hangman's fee.'

Then Robin he turns him round about,
  And jumps from stock to stone;
'By the truth of my body,' the Sheriff he said,
  'That's well jumped, thou nimble old man!'

'I was ne'er a hangman in all my life,
  Nor yet intend to trade;
But cursed be he,' said bold Robin Hood,
  'That first a hangman was made!

'I've a bag for meal, and a bag for malt,
  And a bag for barley and corn;
A bag for bread, a bag for meat,
  And a bag for my little small horn.

73

'I have a horn in my pockèt,
      I got it from Robin Hood,
And still when I set it to my mouth
      For thee it blows no good.'

The first loud blast that he did blow,
      He blew both loud and shrill;
A hundred and fifty of Robin Hood's men
      Came riding over the hill.

The next loud blast that he did give,
      He blew both loud and amain;
And quickly sixty of Robin Hood's men
      Came shining over the plain.

'O who are yon,' the Sheriff he said,
      'Come tripping over the lea?'
'They're my attendants,' bold Robin did say,
      'They'll pay a visit to thee.'

They took the gallows from its place,
      They set it in the glen,
They hanged the proud Sheriff on that,
      And released their own three men.

Robin Hood
and the Bishop of Hereford

Come, gentlemen all, and listen a while,
      A story I'll to you unfold:
How the Bishop was served by bold Robin Hood,
      When he robbed him of his gold.

As it befell in merry Barnsdale,
      And under the green-wood tree,
The Bishop of Hereford was to come by,
      With all his companỳ.

'Come, kill us a ven'son,' said bold Robin Hood,
  'Come, kill me a good fat deer;
The Bishop's to dine with me today,
  And he shall pay well for his cheer.

'We'll kill a fat ven'son,' said bold Robin Hood,
  'And dress't by the highway-side,
And watch for the Bishop narrowly,
  Lest some other way he should ride.

He dressed himself up in shepherd's attire,
  With six of his men alsò;
And the Bishop of Hereford came that way,
  As about the fire they did go.

'What matter is this?' said the Bishop then,
  'Or for whom do you make this a-do?
Or why do you kill the King's ven'son,
  When your company is so few?'

'We are shepherds,' said bold Robin Hood,
  'And we keep sheep all the year;
And we are disposed to be merry this day,
  And to kill of the King's fat deer.'

'You are brave fellows!' said the Bishòp,
  'And the King of your doings shall know;
Therefore make haste, come along with me,
  For before the King you shall go.'

'O pardon, O pardon,' says brave Robin Hood,
  'O pardon, I thee pray!
For it never becomes your lordship's coat
  To take men's lives away.'

'No pardon, no pardon!' the Bishop says then,
  'No pardon I thee owe;
Therefore make haste, come along with me,
  For before the King you shall go.'

Robin set his back against a tree,
   And his foot against a thorn,
And from underneath his shepherd's coat,
   He pulled a bugle horn.

He put the little end to his mouth,
   And a loud blast did he blow,
Till three score and ten of bold Robin's men
   Came running all on a row.

All making obeisance to bold Robin Hood,
   'Twas a comely sight to see:
'What matter, my master,' said Little John,
   'That you blow so hastilỳ?'

'O here is the Bishop of Hereford,
   And no pardon we shall have.'
'Cut off his head,' said Little John,
   'And throw him into his grave!'

'O pardon, O pardon,' the Bishop said then.
   'O pardon, I thee pray!
For if I'd have known it had been you,
   I'd have gone some other way.'

'No pardon, no pardon!' said bold Robin Hood,
   'No pardon I thee owe;
Therefore make haste, come along with me,
   For to merry Barnsdale you shall go.'

Then Robin has taken the Bishop's hand,
   And led him to merry Barnsdale;
He made him to stay and sup with him,
   And to drink wine, beer, and ale.

'Call in the reckoning,' then said the Bishòp,
   'For methinks it grows wondrous high.'
'Lend me your purse, Bishop,' said Little John,
   And I'll tell you by-and-by.'

Then Little John took the Bishop's cloak,
   And spread it upon the ground,
And out of the Bishop's portmanteàu
   He took three hundred pound.

'So now let him go,' said Robin Hood;
   Said Little John, 'That may not be;
For I vow and protest he shall sing us a mass
   Before that he go from me!'

Robin Hood took the Bishop by the hand,
   And bound him fast to a tree,
And made him to sing a mass, God wot,
   To him and his yeomanrỳ.

Then Robin Hood brought him through the wood,
   And causèd the music to play,
And they made the Bishop to dance in his boots,
   And they set him on's dapple-grey;
And they gave him the tail to hold in his hand,
   And glad he could so get away.

The Death of Robin Hood

When Robin Hood and Little John
   Down a-down, a-down, a-down
   Went o'er yon bank of broom,
Said Robin Hood to Little John,
   'We have shot for many a pound,
   Hey! down a-down, a-down!

'But I am not able to shoot one shot more,
   My proud arrows will not flee;
But I have a cousin lives down below,
   Please God, she will now bleed me.

77

'I will never eat nor drink,' he said,
   Nor meat will do me good,
Till I have been to merry Kirkleys
   My veins for to let blood.

'The dame prior is my aunt's daughter,
   And nigh unto my kin;
I know she would do me no harm this day,
   For all the world to win.'

'That I advise not,' said Little John,
   'Master, by the assent of me,
Without half a hundred of your best bowmen
   You take to go with ye.'

'If thou be afeared, thou Little John,
   At home I bid thee be.'
'If you be wroth, my dear master,
   'You shall never hear more of me.'

Now Robin is gone to merry Kirkleys,
   Down a-down, a-down, a-down,
   And there he knockèd upon the pin;
Up then rose Dame Priorèss,
   And let good Robin in.
   Hey! down a-down, a-down!

Then Robin gave to Dame Priorèss
   Twenty pounds in gold,
And bade her spend while that did last,
   She should have more when she would.

'Will you please to sit down, cousin Robin,
   And drink some beer with me?'
'No, I will neither eat nor drink
   Till I am blooded by thee.'

Down then came Dame Priorèss,
  Down she came full quick,
With a pair of blood-irons in her hands
  Were wrappèd all in silk.

'Set a chafing-dish to the fire,' she said,
  'And strip thou up thy sleeve.'
(I hold him but an unwise man
  That will no warning believe.)

79

She laid the blood-irons to Robin's vein,
  Alack, the more pitỳ!
And pierced the vein, and let out the blood
  That full red was to see.

And first it bled the thick, thick blood,
  And afterwards the thin.
And well then wist good Robin Hood
  Treason was there within.

And there she blooded bold Robin Hood
  While one drop of blood would run;
There he did bleed the live-long day,
  Until the next at noon.

He bethought him then of the casement there,
  Being locked up in the room;
But so weak was he, he could not leap,
  He could not get him down.

He bethought him then of his bugle-horn,
  That hung low down to his knee;
He set his horn unto his mouth,
  And blew out weak blasts three.

Then Little John he heard the horn,
  Where he sat under a tree;
'I fear my master is now near dead,
  He blows so wearilỳ.'
  *Down a-down, a-down, a-down,
  Hey! down a-down, a-down.*

Little John is gone to merry Kirkleys,
  As fast as fast can be,
And when he came to merry Kirkleys
  He broke locks two or three.

Until he came bold Robin unto,
  Then he fell on his knee;
'A boon, a boon!' cries Little John,
  'Master, I beg of thee!'

'What is that boon,' said Robin Hood,
  'That thou dost beg of me?'
'It is to burn fair Kirkleys-hall,
  And all their nunnerỳ.'

'Now nay, now nay,' quoth Robin Hood,
  'That boon I'll not grant thee;
I never hurt woman in all my life,
  Nor men in their companỳ.

'I never hurt maid in all my life,
  Nor at my end shall it be,
But give me my bent bow in my hand,
  And a broad arrow I'll let flee;
And where that arrow is taken up
  There shall my grave digged be.

'Lay me a green sod under my head,
  Another at my feet,
And lay my bent bow at my side,
  Which was my music sweet;
And make my grave of gravel and green,
  Which is most right and meet.

'Let me have length and breadth enough,
  And under my head a sod;
That they may say when I am dead,
  "Here lies bold Robin Hood!"'
  Down a-down, a-down, a-down,
  Hey! down a-down, a-down.

Maiden in the Moor

Maiden in the moor lay,
In the moor lay,
Seven nights full, seven nights full
Maiden in the moor lay,
In the moor lay,
Seven nights full and a day.

Well, what was her meat,
What was her meat?
The primrose and the—
The primrose and the—
Well, what was her meat,
What was her meat?
The primrose and the violet.

Well, what was her drink,
What was her drink?
The cold water of the—
The cold water of the—
Well, what was her drink,
What was her drink?
The cold water of the well-spring.

Well, what was her bower,
What was her bower?
The red rose and the—
The red rose and the—
Well, what was her bower,
What was her bower?
The red rose and the lily flower.

Two Rivers

Says Tweed to Till:
'What makes you run so still?
Says Till to Tweed:
'Though you run with speed,
And I run slow,
For one man that you drown
I drown two.'

The Ghost's Lament

Woe's me, woe's me,
The acorn's not yet
Fallen from the tree,
That's to grow the oak,
That's to make the cradle,
That's to rock the bairn,
That's to grow a man
That's to lay me.

The False Knight upon the Road

'O where are you going?'
    Quoth the false knight upon the road.
'I'm going to the school,'
    Quoth the wee boy, and still he stood.

'What is that upon your back?'
    Quoth the false knight upon the road.
'Truly it is my books,'
    Quoth the wee boy, and still he stood.

'What's that you've got in your arm?'
    Quoth the false knight upon the road.
'Truly it's peat for the school fire,'
    Quoth the wee boy, and still he stood.

'Who owns they sheep?'
    Quoth the false knight upon the road.
'They're mine and my mother's,'
    Quoth the wee boy, and still he stood.

'How many of them are mine?'
    Quoth the false knight upon the road.
'All they that have blue tails,'
    Quoth the wee boy, and still he stood.

'I wish you were on yon tree,'
  Quoth the false knight upon the road.
'And a good ladder under me,'
  Quoth the wee boy, and still he stood.

'And the ladder for to break,'
  Quoth the false knight upon the road.
'And *you* for to fall down,'
  Quoth the wee boy, and still he stood.

'I wish you were in yon sea,'
  Quoth the false knight upon the road.
'And a good ship under me,'
  Quoth the wee boy, and still he stood.

'And the ship for to break,'
  Quoth the false knight upon the road.
'And *you* to be drowned,'
  Quoth the wee boy, and still he stood.

The Crow and the Crane

As I passed by a river side,
  And there as I did go,
An argument I chanced to hear
  Between a Crane and Crow.

The Crow said unto the Crane,
  'If all the world should turn,
Before we had the Father,
  And now we have the Son!

'From whence does the Son come?
  From where and from what place?'
The Crow said, 'In a manger
  Between an ox and ass.'

'Where is the golden cradle
  That Christ was rockèd in?
Where are the silken sheets
  That Jesus was wrapped in?'

'A manger was the cradle
  That Christ was rockèd in;
The provender the asses left
  So sweetly he slept on.

'There was a star in the West Land,
  So bright did it appear
Into King Herod's chamber
  And where King Herod were.

'The Wise Men soon espied it,
  And told the King on high,
A princely babe was born that night
  No king could e'er destroy.

' "If this be true," King Herod said,
   "As thou tellest unto me,
This roasted cock that lies in the dish
   Shall crow out loud times three."

'The cock soon freshly feathered was
   By the work of God's own hand,
And then three times he crowèd loud
   In the dish where he did stand.

' "Rise up, rise up, you merry men all,
   See that you ready be,
All children under two years old,
   Now slain they all shall be!"

'Then Jesus, ah! and Joseph,
   And Mary that was so pure,
They travelled into Egypt,
   As you shall find it sure.

'And when they came to Egypt's land,
   Amongst those fierce wild beasts,
Mary, she being weary,
   Must needs sit down and rest.

' "Come sit thee down," says Jesus,
   "Come sit thee down by me,
And thou shalt see how these wild beasts
   Do come and worship me."

'First came the lovely lion,
   Of Jesus grace asking;
And of the wild beasts in the field,
   The lion shall be king.

'Then Jesus, ah! and Joseph,
   And Mary without a stain,
They travelled by a husbandman,
   As he did sow his grain.

' "God speed thee, man!" said Jesus,
    "Go fetch thy ox and wain,
The corn which thou this day hast sown
    Now carry home again.

' "If any one should come this way,
    And where I am would know,
Tell them that Jesus passèd by
    As thou thy seed didst sow."

'After that came King Herod,
    With his train so furiously,
Inquiring of the husbandman
    If Jesus he did see.

' "Why, the truth it must be spoken,
    And the truth it must be known,
For Jesus passèd by this way
    Just as my seed was sown.

' "But now I have it reapen,
    And some laid on my wain,
Ready to fetch and carry
    Into my barn again."

' "Turn back," says the Captain,
    "Your labour and mine's in vain;
It's full three-quarters of a year
    Since he has sown his grain."

'So Herod was deceivèd,
    By the work of God's own hand,
And farther he pursued them not
    Into Egypt's land.'

I Sing of a Maiden

I sing of a maiden
  That is matchless,
King of all kings
  For her son she chose.

He came all so still
  Where his mother was,
As dew in April
  That falleth on the grass.

He came all so still
  To his mother's bower,
As dew in April
  That falleth on the flower.

He came all so still
  Where his mother lay,
As dew in April
  That falleth on the spray.

Mother and maiden
  Was never none but she;
Well may such a lady
  God's mother be.

Jolly Wat

Can I not sing but 'Hoy',
When the jolly shepherd made so much joy?

The shepherd upon a hill he sat,
He had on him his coat and hat,
His tar-box, his pipe and his flask he had;
His name was callèd Jolly Jolly Wat,
    For he was a good herdsman's boy.
        Ut hoy!
    For in his pipe he made so much joy.

The shepherd upon a hill him laid,
His dog unto his girdle was tied,
He had slept not very long
When '*Gloria in excelsis*' was to him sung.
        Ut hoy!
  For in his pipe he made so much joy.

The shepherd on a hill he stood,
Round about him his sheep they trod,
He put his hand under his hood,
He saw a star as red as blood.
        Ut hoy!
  For in his pipe he made so much joy.

The shepherd said anon right,
'I will go see yon wondrous sight,
The angel singing from the height,
And the star that shines so bright!'
        Ut hoy!
  For in his pipe he made so much joy.

'Now farewell, Mall, and also Will,
For love of me keep ye all still,
Until I come be ye all well,
And evermore, Will, ring loud thy bell.'
        Ut hoy!
  For in his pipe he made so much joy.

'Now I must go where Christ is born,
Farewell! until tomorrow morn.
Dog, keep well my sheep from the corn,
And warn well "warroke" when I blow my horn!'
        Ut hoy!
  For in his pipe he made so much joy.

When Wat to Bethlehem come was,
He sweat, he had gone faster than a pace;

He found Jesu in a simple place,
Between an ox but and an ass.
>> *Ut hoy!*
For in his pipe he made so much joy.

'Jesu, I offer thee here my pipe,
My skirt, my tar-box, and my scrip,
Home to my fellows now will I skip,
And also look unto my sheep.'
>> *Ut hoy!*
For in his pipe he made so much joy.

'Now farewell, mine own herdsman Wat.'
'Yea, 'fore God, Lady, I am called that.
Lull well Jesu in thy lap,
And farewell, Joseph, in thy round cap!'
>> *Ut hoy!*
For in his pipe he made so much joy.

'Now may I well both hope and sing,
For I have been at Christ's bearing;
Home to my fellows now will I fling,
Christ of heaven to his bliss us bring!'
>> *Ut hoy!*
For in his pipe he made so much joy.

Clootie

There came a knight from out the west,
 Jennifer, Gentle and Rosemary,
I wot he was but an uncouth guest,
 As the dove flies over the mulberry tree.

He came unto a widow's door,
 Jennifer, Gentle and Rosemary,
And asked where her three daughters were,
 As the dove flies over the mulberry tree.

'The eldest's to the washing gone,'
 Jennifer, Gentle and Rosemary,
'The second's to the baking gone,'
 As the dove flies over the mulberry tree.

'The youngest one's to a wedding gone,'
 Jennifer, Gentle and Rosemary,
'And it will be night ere she comes home,'
 As the dove flies over the mulberry tree.

He sat him down upon a stone,
 Jennifer, Gentle and Rosemary,
Till these three maidens came tripping home,
 As the dove flies over the mulberry tree.

The eldest one she let him in,
 Jennifer, Gentle and Rosemary,
And pinned the door with a silver pin;
 As the dove flies over the mulberry tree.

The second one she made his bed,
 Jennifer, Gentle and Rosemary,
And laid soft pillows for his head;
 As the dove flies over the mulberry tree.

The youngest one was bold and bright,
   Jennifer, Gentle and Rosemary,
And she tarried for words with this uncouth knight,
   As the dove flies over the mulberry tree.

'Now questions ten you shall answer me,'
   Jennifer, Gentle and Rosemary,
'Or else, fair maid, you must marry me.'
   As the dove flies over the mulberry tree.

95

'O what is higher than the tree?'
Jennifer, Gentle and Rosemary,
'And what is deeper than the sea?'
As the dove flies over the mulberry tree.

'Or what is heavier than the lead?'
Jennifer, Gentle and Rosemary,
'Or what is better than the bread?'
As the dove flies over the mulberry tree

'Or what is whiter than the milk?'
Jennifer, Gentle and Rosemary,
'Or what is softer than the silk?'
As the dove flies over the mulberry tree.

'Or what is sharper than a thorn?'
Jennifer, Gentle and Rosemary,
'Or what is louder than a horn?'
As the dove flies over the mulberry tree.

'Or what is greener than the grass?'
Jennifer, Gentle and Rosemary,
'Or what is worse than a woman was?'
As the dove flies over the mulberry tree.

'O heaven is higher than the tree,'
Jennifer, Gentle and Rosemary,
'And hell is deeper than the sea,'
As the dove flies over the mulberry tree.

'O sin is heavier than the lead,'
Jennifer, Gentle and Rosemary,
'The blessings better than the bread,'
As the dove flies over the mulberry tree.

'The snow is whiter than the milk,'
Jennifer, Gentle and Rosemary,
'And the down is softer than the silk,'
As the dove flies over the mulberry tree.

'Hunger is sharper than a thorn,'
  Jennifer, Gentle and Rosemary,
'And shame is louder than the horn,'
  As the dove flies over the mulberry tree.

'The parrot's greener than the grass,'
  Jennifer, Gentle and Rosemary,
'And Clootie's worse than a woman was.'
  As the dove flies over the mulberry tree.

As soon as she the fiend did name,
  Jennifer, Gentle and Rosemary,
He flew away in a blazing flame,
  As the dove flies over the mulberry tree.

Chevy Chase

THE FIRST FYTTE

The Percy out of Northumberland
  A vow to God made he
That he would hunt in the mountains
  Of Cheviot within days three,
In spite of doughty Douglas
  And all that e'er with him be.

The fattest harts in all Cheviot
  He would kill and carry away.
'By my faith,' said the doughty Douglas again,
  'I will stop that hunt if I may!'

Then the Percy out of Bamborough came
  With a mighty companỳ,
With fifteen hundred archers bold,
  Chosen from out shires three.

97

This began on a Monday at morn,
  In Cheviot the hills so free;
The child may rue that is unborn,
  It was the more pity.

The drivers through the woods they went
  All for to raise the deer;
Bowmen bickered upon the bent
  With their broad arrows clear.

Harts running through the woods in droves
  On every side appear;
The greyhounds darting through the groves
  All for to kill their deer.

This began in Cheviot, the hills aboon,
  Early on a Monday;
When that it drew to the hour of noon
  A hundred fat harts dead there lay.

They blew a 'mort' upon the bent,
  And from all sides they came;
The Percy to the quarry went
  For to cut up the game.

He said, 'It was the Douglas' promise
  To meet me here this day;
But I knew he would fail, now verily—'
  A great oath then the Percy did say.

At the last a squire of Northumberland,
  Over his shoulder looked he;
He was ware of the doughty Douglas coming,
  With a great company.

With spear and arrow, bill and brand,
  'Twas a mighty sight to see,
Hardier men both of heart and hand
  Were not in Christiantìe.

The doughty Douglas on a steed
  Did ride his men before,
Like a live coal all glittering
  Was the armour that he wore.

'Leave cutting up the deer,' he said,
  'To your bows look you take good heed;
For since you were of your mothers born
  You never had so much need.

'Tell me whose men ye are,' says he,
  'Or whose men that ye be.
Who gave you leave in this Cheviot chase
  In spite of mine and me?'

The first man that him answer made,
  It was good Lord Percy:
'We will not tell whose men we are,
  Nor whose men that we be;
But we will hunt here in this chase
  In spite of thine and thee.

99

'The fattest harts in Cheviot
   We have killed, to carry away.'
'By my troth,' said the doughty Douglas again,
   'The one of us dies this day!'

'But to kill all these guiltless men,
   Alas, were great pitỳ!
But, Percy, thou art a lord of land,
   I am earl in my countrỳ—
Let all our men in a party stand,
   And do battle but thee and me.'

'Christ's curse on his crown,' said the Lord Percy,
   'Whosoever thereto says nay!
By my troth, thou doughty Douglas,' he says,
   'Thou shalt never see that day,

'Neither in England, Scotland, nor France,
   Nor for no man of woman born,
But, and fortune be my chance,
   I dare meet him, one man for one!'

Then bespake a squire of Northumberland,
   Richard Witherington was his name,
'It shall never be told in South England,
   To King Harry the Fourth, for shame!

'I wot that you be two great lords,
   I am a poor squire of land;
I will never see my captain fight on a field,
   And I look on and stand.
But while I may my weapon wield
   I'll not fail, both heart and hand.'

That day, that day, that dreadful day!
   The first fytte here I find;
If you'll hear any more of the hunting of Cheviot,
   Yet there is more behind.

THE SECOND FYTTE

The Englishmen had their bows bent,
　Their hearts were good and true;
The first of arrows that they shot off,
　Seven score spearmen they slew.

The Douglas parted his host in three,
　Like a chief chieftain of pride;
With sure spears of mighty tree
　They came in on every side;

And through the English archery
　Gave many a wound full wide,
Many doughty men they made to die,
　Which gainèd them no pride.

The Englishmen let their good bows be,
　And pulled out brands that were bright;
It was a heavy sight to see
　Bright swords on steel caps light.

Right through rich mail and long gauntlet
  They struck with might and main;
Many a man that was full free
  There under foot was lain.

At last the Douglas and Percy met,
  The captains man to man;
They smote together until they sweat
  With swords of fine Milan.

These worthy warriors for to fight,
  Thereto they were full fain,
Till the blood out of their steel caps splashed
  As ever did hail or rain.

'Yield thee, Percy,' said the Douglas,
  'And in faith I shall thee bring
Where thou shalt have an earl's wages
  Of Jamie, our Scottish king.

'Thou shalt have thy ransom free,
  I promise thee here this thing;
For the manfullest man thou art that e'er
  I conquered in field fighting.'

But 'Nay,' then said the lord Percy,
  'I told it thee before
That I would never yielded be
  To man that woman bore.'

With that an arrow came hastily
  Forth of a mighty throng,
And it hath stricken the Earl Douglas
  In at the breast-bone strong.

Through his liver and both his lungs
  The sharp arrow is gone,
That never after in his life-days,
  He spake more words but one:

Twas, 'Fight ye, my merry men, while ye may,
  For my life-days be done!'

The Percy leaned upon his brand,
  And saw the Douglas die,
He took the dead man by the hand,
  And said, 'Woe, woe am I!

'To have saved thy life I'd have parted with
  My lands for full years three;
For a better man of heart nor of hand
  Was not in the north countrỳ.'

All this there saw a Scottish knight,
  Sir Hugh the Montgomerỳ,
When he saw the Douglas done to death,
  Through a hundred archerỳ
He never stayed nor he never stopped
  Till he came to the Lord Percỳ.

He set upon the Lord Percy
  A blow that was full sore;
With a sure spear of a mighty tree
  Through the body he him bore;
On the other side a man might see
  A large cloth-yard or more.

An archer of Northumberland
  Saw slain the Lord Percỳ,
He bore a bent bow in his hand,
  Was made of a trusty tree.

An arrow that was a cloth-yard long,
  To the hard steel pulled he;
A blow that was both sad and sore
  He set on Montgomerỳ.

103

The blow it was both sad and sore,
  That he on Montgomery set;
The swan-feathers that his arrow bore
  With his heart-blood they were wet.

There was never a man one foot would flee,
  But stout in press did stand,
Hewing on each other whilst they might
  With many a baleful brand.

This battle began in Cheviot
  An hour before the noon;
And when the even-song bell was rung
  The battle was not half done.

They took their stand on either hand
  All by the fair moon's light;
Many had no strength to stand
  On Cheviot hills that night.

Of fifteen hundred archers of England,
  Went away but seventy and three,
Of twenty hundred spearmen of Scotland,
  But even five and fifty.

For Witherington my heart was woe,
  That ever he slain should be;
For when both his legs were hewn in two
  Yet he kneeled and fought on his knee.

So on the morrow they made them biers
  Of birch and hazel so grey;
Many widows with weeping tears
  Came to fetch their mates away.

Teviotdale may talk of care,
  Northumberland may make moan;
For two such captains as slain were there
  On the Border shall never be known.

Word is come to Edinburgh,
  To Jamie, the Scottish King,
Earl Douglas, lieutenant of the Marches,
  Lay slain Cheviot within.

His hands the King did clench and wring,
  Said, 'Alas! and woe is me!
Such another captain Scotland within
  I' faith shall never be!'

Word is come to lovely London,
  To the fourth Harry, our King,
Lord Percy, lieutenant of the Marches,
  Lay slain Cheviot within.

'God have mercy on his soul!' said King Harry,
  'Good Lord, if thy will it be!
I've a hundred captains in England,' he said,
  'As good as ever was he.
But Percy, as I brook my life,
  Thy death well quit shall be!'

This was the hunting of the Cheviot—
  That ever began this turn!
Old men that know well the ground,
  Call it of Otterburn.

There was never a time on the Border-lands,
  Since the Douglas and Percy met,
But 'tis marvel if the red blood run not
  As the rain does in the street.

Jesu Christ, our woes relieve,
  And to the bliss us bring!
This was the hunting of the Cheviot,
  God send us all good ending!

Johnie
Faa

The gipsies came to our good lord's gate,
   And O but they sang sweetly!
They sang so sweet, and so very complete
   That down came the fair lady.

And she came tripping down the stair,
   And all her maids before her;
As soon as they saw her well-favoured face
   They cast the glamour o'er her.

'O come with me,' says Johnie Faa,
   'O come with me, my dearie;
For I vow and I swear by the hilt of my sword
   That your lord shall no more come near ye.'

Then she gave them the red, red wine,
   And they gave her the gingers;
But she gave them a far better thing—
   The seven gold rings from her fingers.

'Go take from me this gay mantle,
   And bring to me a plaidie;
For if kith and kin and all had sworn,
   I'll follow the gipsy laddie.

'Yestreen I rode this water deep,
   And my own good lord beside me,
But this night I must wet my little pretty feet,
   With a pack of blackguards to guide me.

'Yestreen I lay in a well-made bed,
   With my good lord beyond me;
This night I'll lie in the ash-corner,
   With the gipsies all around me.

'I'll make a cloak for my Johnie Faa,
    I'll make a cloak for my dearie;
And he'll get all the sash goes round,
    And my lord shall no more come near me!'

And when our lord came home at e'en,
    And asked for his fair lady,
The one she cried, and the other replied,
    'She's away with the gipsy laddie!'

'Go saddle me the black, black steed,
    Go saddle and make him ready;
Before that I either eat or sleep
    I'll go seek my fair lady.'

And we were fifteen well-made men,
    Although we were not bonny;
And we were all put down but one,
    For a fair young wanton lady.

Alison Gross

O Alison Gross that lives in yon tower,
　　The ugliest witch in the north countrỳ,
Has trysted me one day up to her bower,
　　And many fair speeches she made to me.

She stroked my head and she combed my hair,
　　And she set me down softly on her knee;
Says, 'If you will be my sweetheart so true,
　　So many fine things I will give to thee.'

She showed me a mantle of red scarlèt,
　　With golden flowers and fringes fine;
Says, 'If you will be my sweetheart so true,
　　This goodly gift it shall be thine.'

'Away, away, you ugly witch,
　　Hold far away, and let me be!
I never will be your sweetheart so true,
　　And I wish I were out of your companỳ.'

She next brought a shirt of the softest silk,
　　Well wrought with pearls about the band;
Says, 'If you will be my sweetheart so true,
　　This goodly gift you shall command.'

She showed me a cup of the good red gold,
    Well set with jewels so fair to see;
Says, 'If you will be my sweetheart so true,
    This goodly gift I will give to thee.'

'Away, away, you ugly witch,
    Hold far away, and let me be!
I would not once kiss your ugly mouth
    For all the gold in the north countrỳ.'

She's turned her right and round about,
    And thrice she blew on a grass-green horn;
And she swore by the moon and the stars above
    That she'd make me rue the day I was born.

Then out she has taken a silver wand,
    And she's turned her three times round and round;
She muttered such words that my strength it failed,
    And I fell down senseless on the ground.

She's turned me into an ugly worm,
    And made me toddle about the tree;
And aye, on every Saturday night,
    My sister Maisry came to me,

With silver basin and silver comb,
    To comb my headie upon her knee;
But before I'd have kissed with Alison Gross,
    I'd sooner have toddled about the tree.

But as it fell out, on last Hallowe'en,
    When the Fairy Court came riding by,
The Queen lighted down on a flowery bank,
    Not far from the tree where I used to lie.

She took me up in her milk-white hand,
    And she's stroked me three times over her knee;
She changed me again to my own proper shape,
    And no more I toddle about the tree.

The Heir of Linne

The bonny heir, the well-favoured heir,
   The weary heir of Linne:
Yonder he stands at his father's gate,
   And nobody bids him in.

O see where he goes, and see where he stands,
   The unthrifty heir of Linne!
O see where he stands on the cold causeway,
   And none bids him come in.

His father and mother both were dead,
   And so was the head of his kin;
To the cards and dice then he did run,
   The bonny heir of Linne.

To drink the wine that was so clear
   With all he made merrỳ;
And then bespake him John of Scales,
   To the heir of Linne said he,

'How dost thou now, thou heir of Linne,
   Dost want or gold or fee?
Wilt thou not sell thy lands so broad
   To such a good fellow as me?'

He told the gold upon the board,
   Lacked never a bare pennỳ:
'The gold is thine, the land is mine,
   The Lord of Linne I will be.'

'Here's gold enough,' says the heir of Linne,
   For me and my companỳ.'
He drank the wine that was so clear,
   And he lived merrilỳ.

Within three quarters of a year,
  His gold it waxèd thin;
His merry men they gave him jeers,
  'To the devil with you, heir of Linne!'

'Now well-a-day!' said the heir of Linne,
  'I have left not one pennỳ.
God be with my father,' he said,
  'On his land he lived merrilỳ.'

His nurse out at her window looked,
  Beholding dale and down,
And she beheld this distressed young man
  Come walking to the town.

O see where he goes, and see where he stands,
   The weary heir of Linne!
O see where he stands on the cold causeway,
   And none bids him come in!'

'Sing o'er again that song, my nurse,
   And sing it clear and plain.'
'I never sang song in all my life,
   But I'd sing it to you again.'

'Come here, come here now, Willy,' she said,
   'And rest yourself with me.
I have seen you in far better days,
   And in jovial companỳ.'

'Give me a slice of your bread, my nurse,
   And a bottle of your wine,
And I will pay it you o'er again,
   When I am Lord of Linne.'

'Ye'll get a slice of my bread, Willy,
   And a bottle of my wine;
But you'll pay me when the seas go dry,
   For ye'll ne'er be Lord of Linne.'

Then he turned him right and round about,
   As a mother's son will do;
And off he set and bent his way,
   The house of Linne came to.

But when to that good castle he came,
   They were set down to dine;
A score of nobles there he saw,
   Sat drinking at their wine.

Then some bade give him beef and fish,
   And some but bone and fin;
And some they bade give nothing at all
   To the weary heir of Linne.

Then out it speaks him John of Scales,
  A saucy word did he say:
'Put round the cup, give the beggar a sup,
  And let him go his way.'

O he turned him right and round about,
  As a mother's son will do;
Then minded him on a little wee key
  His mother left him to.

His mother left him this little wee key,
  And bid him take good heed:
'Keep you this little wee key,' she said,
  'Till you are in most need.'

Then forth he went, these nobles left
  Drinking within the hall;
With a walking-rod into his hand,
  He walked the castle all.

Till that he came to a little wee door,
  And therein slipped the key,
And there he found three chests were full
  Of red and white monèy.

Back then to the hall he went,
  As fast as fast could be;
Until he came where John of Scales
  Sat drinking merrilỳ.

Then out it spake him John of Scales,
  He spake with mock and jeer:
'I'd give a seat to the Lord of Linne,
  If so be that he were here!

'When the lands of Linne a-selling were,
  All men said they were free;
I will sell them twenty pounds better cheap
  Than I bought them of thee.'

'I take ye to witness nobles all!'
  (He threw down a luck-pennỳ),
'I will buy them twenty pounds better cheap
  Than he bought them of me.'

He's gone him to the gaming-table,
  Was fair and clean to see;
And there he's told as much rich gold
  As the lands of Linne made free.

He told the gold there over the board,
  Lacked never a broad pennỳ:
'The gold is thine, the land is mine,
  Lord of Linne again I'll be.'

'Well-a-day!' said John of Scales' wife,
  'Well-a-day, and woe is me!
Last night I was the Lady of Linne,
  And now I'm a nobodỳ!'

'But fare thee well,' said the heir of Linne,
  'Now John of Scales!' said he.
'A curse light on me if ever again,
  My lands be in jeopardỳ!'

Sweet William's Ghost

There came a ghost to Margret's door,
  With many a grievous groan,
And aye he twirlèd at the pin,
  But answer made she none.

'Is it my father Philip?
  Or is't my brother John?
Or is't my true love Willie,
  From Scotland new come home?'

' 'Tis not thy father Philip,
  Nor yet thy brother John,
But 'tis thy true love Willie,
  From Scotland new come home.

'O sweet Margret! O dear Margret!
  I pray thee speak to me;
Give me my faith and troth, Margret,
  As I gave it to thee.'

'Thy faith and troth thou'lt never get,
  Of me shalt never win,
Till that thou come within my bower,
  And kiss me cheek and chin.'

'If I should come within thy bower,
    I am no earthly man;
And should I kiss thy rosy lips,
    Thy days would not be long.

'O sweet Margret! O dear Margret!
    I pray thee speak to me;
Give me my faith and troth, Margret,
    As I gave it to thee.'

'Thy faith and troth thou'lt never get,
    Of me shalt never win,
Till that thou take me to yon kirkyard,
    And wed me with a ring.'

'My bones are in a kirkyard laid
    Afar beyond the sea;
And it is but my ghost, Margret,
    That's speaking now to thee.'

She's stretchèd out her lily hand,
    As for to do her best:
'Have there your faith and troth, Willie,
    God send your soul good rest!'

She's kilted up her robes of green,
    A piece below her knee:
And all the live-long winter night
    The dead corpse followed she.

'Is there any room at your head, Willie,
    Is there any room at your feet,
Is there any room at your side, Willie,
    Wherein that I may creep?'

'There's no room at my head, Margret,
    There's no room at my feet,
There's no room at my side, Margret,
    My coffin is made so meet.'

Then up and crew the red, red cock,
   And up and crew the grey:
' 'Tis time, 'tis time, my dear Margret,
   That I was gone away.'

No more the ghost to Margret said,
   But with a grievous groan
Evanished in a cloud of mist,
   And left her all alone.

May Colvin

False Sir John a-wooing came,
   To a maid of beauty rare;
May Colvin was this lady's name,
   Her father's only heir.

He woo'd her in bower, he woo'd her in hall,
   He woo'd her aye or nay;
Until he got that lady's consent
   To mount and ride away.

'Go fetch me some of your father's gold,
   And some of your mother's fee;
And I'll carry you into the north land,
   And there I'll wed with thee.'

She's gone to her father's coffers,
   Where all his money lay;
And she's taken the red, and she's left the white,
   And so lightly she's tripped away.

She's gone to her father's stables
   Where all the steeds did stand,
And she's taken the best, and she's left the worst
   That was in her father's land.

She's mounted on a milk-white steed,
   On a dapple-grey mounts he,
And on they rode to a lonesome part,
   A rock beside the sea.

'Leap off the steed,' says false Sir John,
   'Your bridal bed you see;
Seven ladies have I drownèd here,
   And the eighth one you shall be.

'Cast off, cast off your silks so fine,
   And lay them on a stone,
For they are too fine and costly
   To rot in the salt sea foam.

'Cast off, cast off your silken stays,
   Cast off your broidered shoon,
For they are too fine and costly
   To rot in the salt sea foam.

'Cast off, cast off your Holland smock,
   That's bordered with the lawn,
For it is too fine and costly
   To rot in the salt sea foam.'

'O turn about, thou false Sir John,
   And look to the leaf of the tree;
For it never became a gentleman
   A naked woman to see.'

He turned himself straight round about,
   To look to the leaf of the tree;
She's clasped her arms about his waist,
   And thrown him in the sea.

'O hold a grip of me, May Colvin,
   For fear that I should drown;
I'll take you home to your father's bower
   And safe I'll set you down.'

'No help, no help, thou false Sir John,
  No help, no pity thee!
For you lie not in a colder bed
  Than you thought to lay me.'

She mounted on her milk-white steed,
  And led the dapple-grey,
And she rode till she reached her father's gate,
  At the breaking of the day.

Up then spake the pretty parrot,
  'May Colvin, where have you been?
What has become of false Sir John
  That went with you yestreen?'

'O hold your tongue, my pretty parrot,
    Nor tell no tales of me;
Your cage shall be made of the beaten gold,
    And the spokes of ivory.'

Up then spake her father dear,
    In the bed-chamber where he lay:
'What ails the pretty parrot,
    That he prattles so long ere day?'

'There came a cat to my cage, master,
    I thought 'twould have worried me,
And I was calling to May Colvin
    To take the cat from me.'

Glenlogie

Four-and-twenty nobles rode to the King's hall,
But bonny Glenlogie was the flower of them all.

Lady Jeanie Melville came tripping down the stair,
When she saw Glenlogie her heart it grew sore.

She's called to the footman that ran by his side,
Says, 'What is your lord's name, and where does he bide?'

'His name is Glenlogie, when he is from home;
He's of the gay Gordons, his name it is John.'

'Glenlogie, Glenlogie, if you will prove kind,
My love is laid on you; I'm telling my mind.'

He turned about lightly, as all Gordons do,
Says, 'I thank you, Lady Jeanie, but I'm not for you.'

She called on her maidens her bed for to make;
Her rings from her fingers she did them all break.

'Where'll I get a bonny boy, to win hose and shoon,
To go to Glenlogie, and bid Logie come?'

When Glenlogie got the letter, among noblemen,
'I wonder,' says Glenlogie, 'what do young women mean?

'I wonder in the world what do young women see,
That bonny Lady Jeanie should lie down and die for me?

'Go saddle my black horse, go saddle him soon,
Till I ride to Bethelnie, to see Lady Jean!'

When he came to Bethelnie, he rode round about,
And saw Jeanie's father at the window look out.

When he came to the gateway, small mirth was there there,
But weeping and wailing, and tearing of hair.

O pale and wan looked she when Glenlogie came in,
But red ruddy grew she when he sat down.

'Turn round, Jeanie Melville, turn round to this side,
And I'll be the bridegroom, and you'll be the bride!'

O 'twas a merry wedding, and the portion down told,
For bonny Jeanie Melville, scarce sixteen years old!

John Dory

As it fell out on a holy-day,
  And upon a holy-tide-a,
John Dory bought him an ambling nag,
  To Paris for to ride-a.

And when John Dory to Paris was come,
  A little before the gate-a,
John Dory was fitted, the porter was witted
  To let him in thereat-a.

The first man that John Dory did meet,
  Was good King John of France-a;
John Dory knew well of his courtesy,
  But fell down in a trance-a.

'A pardon, a pardon, my liege and my king,
  For my merry men and for me-a,
And all the churls in merry England,
  I'll bring them all bound to thee-a.'

And Nichol was then a Cornish man,
  A little beside Bohyde-a,
He manned him forth a good black bark,
  With fifty good oars of a side-a.

'Run up, my boy, unto the main top,
  And look what thou canst spy-a.'
'Who ho! Who ho! a good ship do I see,
  I trow it be John Dorỳ-a.'

They hoist their sails, both top and top,
  The mizzen and all beside-a,
And every man stood to his lot,
  Whatever should betide-a.

The roaring cannons then were plied,
  And dub-a-dub went the drum-a;
The braying trumpets loud they cried
  To courage both all and some-a.

The grappling-hooks were brought at length,
  The brown bill and the sword-a,
John Dory at length, for all his strength,
  Was clapt fast under board-a.

Tamlane

'O I forbid you maidens all,
   That wear gold in your hair,
To come or go by Carterhaugh,
   For young Tamlane is there.'

Then up and spake her, fair Janet,
   The fairest of all her kin:
'I'll come and go to Carterhaugh,
   And ask no leave of him.'

She's prinked herself, and preened herself,
   And kilted up her gown,
And she's away to Carterhaugh,
   By the low light of the moon.

She had not pulled a rose, a rose,
   A rose but barely one,
When up there starts the young Tamlane,
   Says, 'Lady, let alone.

'What makes you pull the rose, Janet,
   What makes you break the tree,
What makes you come to Carterhaugh
   Without the leave of me?'

'Well may I pull the rose,' she says,
   'And ask no leave of thee;
For Carterhaugh is all my own,
   My daddy gave it me.'

He's ta'en her by the milk-white hand,
   And by the grass-green sleeve,
He's led her to the fairy ground,
   Of her he asked no leave.

'O if my love were an earthly knight,
  As he is an elfin bold,
I would not change my love,' she says,
  'For aught the world can hold.

'But tell me, tell me true, Tamlane,
  For His sake that died on tree,
O were you ever in holy church,
  Or got you Christiantìe?'

'A word I will not lie, Janet,
  The truth I'll tell to thee,
They christened me in holy church,
  As well as they did thee.

'Roxburgh he was my grandfather,
  Took me with him to bide;
And once it fell upon a day,
  As hunting I did ride,

'There came a wind out of the north,
  A sharp wind and a snell,
A dead sleep it came over me,
  And from my horse I fell;
And the Queen of Fairies she took me
  In yon green hill to dwell.

'And never would I tire, Janet,
  In fairy-land to dwell;
But aye, at every seven years,
  They pay a tithe to hell;
And I'm so fair and full of flesh,
  I'm feared 'twill be mysell.

'But this night is Hallowe'en, Janet,
  The morn is Hallowday,

Then win me, win me, if you will,
  For well I know you may.

'This night it is good Hallowe'en,
  When fairy folk do ride,
And they that would their true-love win,
  At Miles Cross they must bide.'

'But how shall I thee know, Tamlane,
  And how shall I win thee,
Among so many unearthly knights,
  The like I ne'er did see?'

'The first troop that passes by,
  Say nay, and let them go;
The next troop that passes by,
  Say nay, and do right so;
The third troop that passes by,
  It's there you shall me know.

'First let pass the black, Janet,
  And then let pass the brown,
But take a grip of the milk-white steed,
  And pull the rider down.

'For some ride on the black, Janet,
  And some ride on the brown,
But I ride on the milk-white steed,
  A gold star on my crown;
Because I was a christened knight
  They give me this renown.

'My right hand will be gloved, Janet,
  My left hand will be bare,
And these the tokens I give thee,
  No doubt I will be there.

126

'You'll pull me from the milk-white steed,
    And let the bridle fall,
The Queen of Elfin she'll cry out
    "He's won amongst us all!"

'They'll turn me in your arms, Janet,
    A lizard and a snake,
But hold me fast, nor let me go,
    And I shall be your mate.

'They'll turn me in your arms, Janet,
    A hot iron in the fire,
But hold me fast, nor let me go,
    To be your heart's desire.

127

'They'll shape me in your arms, Janet,
  A swan, likewise a dove,
But hold me fast, nor let me go,
  To be your own true love.

'And last they'll shape me in your arms
  A mother-naked man;
Cast your green mantle over me,
  And so I shall be won.'

She's prinked herself, and preened herself,
  And kilted up her gown,
And she's away to Miles Cross,
  Between twelve hours and one.

About the dead hour of the night,
  She heard the bridles ring;
And Janet was as glad of that
  As any earthly thing.

And first went by the black, the black,
  And then went by the brown,
But fast she gripped the milk-white steed,
  And pulled the rider down.

She pulled him from the milk-white steed,
  And let the bridle fall,
And up there rose th'unearthly cry,
  'He's won amongst us all!'

They shaped him in fair Janet's arms,
  A lizard and a snake,
But aye she grips and holds him fast,
  That he should be her mate.

They shaped him in her arms two
  A hot iron in the fire;
But aye she grips and holds him fast,
  To be her heart's desire.

They shaped him in her arms then
 A swan, likewise a dove;
She held him fast in every shape,
 To be her own true love.

They shaped him in her arms at last
 A mother-naked man;
She cast her mantle over him,
 And so her love she won.

Up then spake the Queen of Fairies,
 Out of a bush of broom:
'She that has ransomed young Tamlane,
 Has gotten a stately groom.'

Up then spake the Queen of Fairies,
 And an angry woman was she,
'She's taken away the bonniest knight
 In all my companỳ!

'But had I known yestreen, Tamlane,
 What this night I have known,
I'd have taken out thy heart of flesh,
 Put in a heart of stone.

'But had I known, Tamlane,' she says,
 'A lady would ransom thee,
I'd have taken out thy two grey eyes,
 Put in two eyes of tree.

'And had I but the wit, yestreen,
 That I have bought this day,
I'd have paid my tithe seven times to hell,
 Ere you'd been won away.'

The Bonny House
of Airlie

It fell on a day, and a bonny summer day,
   When green grew oats and barley,
That there fell out a great dispute
   Between Argyll and Airlie.

Argyll has raised a hundred men,
   A hundred harnessed rarely,
And he's away by the back of Dunkeld,
   To plunder the castle of Airlie.

Lady Ogilvie looks o'er her bower window,
   And O, but she looks warely,
And there she spied the great Argyll,
   Come to plunder the bonny house of Airlie.

'Come down, come down, my Lady Ogilvie,
   Come down and kiss me fairly.'
'O I would not kiss the false Argyll,
   Though he should not leave a standing stone in Airlie!'

He has taken her by the left shoulder,
   Says, 'Dame, where lies thy dowry?'
'O it's east and west yon wan water side,
   And it's down by the banks of the Airlie.'

They have sought it up, they have sought it down,
   They have sought it most severely;
Till they found it in the fair plum-tree,
   That stands on the bowling-green of Airlie.

He has taken her by the middle so small,
   And O, but she wept sorely!
And he's set her down by the bonny burn-side;
   Till they plundered the castle of Airlie.

'If my good lord had been at home,
    As now he's with King Charlie,
There durst not a Campbell in all Argyll
    Have set foot on the green of Airlie.

'Seven bonny sons I have borne unto him,
    The youngest ne'er saw his daddy;
But though I had a hundred more,
    I'd give them all to King Charlie!'

The Two Corbies

As I was walking all alone,
I heard two corbies making their moan,
The one unto the other did say,
'Where shall we go and dine this day?'

'In behind yon old turf dyke,
I wot there lies a new-slain knight,
And nobody knows that he lies there
But his hawk and his hound and his lady fair.

'His hound is to the hunting gone,
His hawk to fetch the wild-fowl home,
His lady's ta'en another mate,
So we may make our dinner sweet.

'You'll sit on his white neck-bone,
And I'll pick out his bonny blue e'en;
With one lock of his golden hair
We'll thatch our nest when it grows bare.

'Many a one for him makes moan,
But none shall know where he is gone;
O'er his white bones, when they are bare,
The wind shall blow for evermair.'

King Estmere

Hearken to me, gentlemen,
  Come and you shall hear;
I'll tell you of two of the boldest brothers
  That ever living were.

The one of them was Adler Younge,
  The other was King Estmere;
They were as bold men of their deeds
  As any were, far or near.

As they were drinking ale and wine,
  Within King Estmere's hall,
'When will you marry a wife, brother,
  A wife to glad us all?'

Then bespake him King Estmere,
  And answered him heartily:
'I know not that lady in any land,
  That's able to marry with me.'

'King Adland hath a daughter, brother,
  Men call her bright and sheen,
If I were king here in your stead,
  That lady should be my queen.'

Says: 'Tell me, tell me, dear brother,
  Throughout merry Englànd,
Were might we find a messenger
  Betwixt us two to send?'

Says: 'You shall ride yourself, brother,
  I'll bear you companỳ;
Many a man through false messengers is deceived,
  And I fear lest so should we.'

Thus they arrayed themselves to ride
   On two good harnessed steeds,
And when they came to King Adland's hall
   Of red gold shone their weeds.

And when they came to King Adland's hall,
   Before the goodly gate,
There they found good King Adlànd,
   Leaning himself thereat.

'Now Christ thee save, good King Adlànd,
   Now Christ you save and see!'
Said, 'You be welcome, King Estmere,
   Right heartily to me.'

'You have a daughter,' said Adler Younge,
   'Men call her bright and sheen;
My brother would marry her to his wife,
   Of England to be queen.'

'Yesterday was at my daughter dear
   Bremor, the King of Spain,
And then she said to him of nay,
   And I doubt she'll do you the same.'

'The King of Spain is a foul paynim,
   And believeth on Mahound,
And pity it were that fair lady
   Should marry a heathen hound.

'But grant to me,' says King Estmere,
   'For my love, I you pray,
That I may see your daughter dear,
   Before I go hence away.'

Down then came that maiden fair,
   With ladies lacèd small,
And half a hundred of bold knights
   To bring her from bower to hall,
And as many gentle squires
   To wait upon them all.

134

Her golden hair that glittered bright
  Hanged low down to her knee,
And every ring on her fingers small
  Shone of the crystal free.

Says, 'God you save, my dear madam,'
  Says, 'God you save and see!'
Said, 'You be welcome, King Estmere,
  Right welcome unto me.

'And if you love me, as you say,
  So well and heartilỳ,
All that ever you've come about
  Soon sped now it shall be.'

Then bespake her father dear:
  'My daughter, I say nay:
Remember well the King of Spain,
  What he said yesterday.

'He would pull down my halls and castles,
  And rob me of my life;
I cannot blame him if he do,
  If I rob him of his wife.'

'Your castles and your towers, father,
  Are strongly built about,
And so of Bremor, King of Spain,
  We need not stand in doubt.

'Plight me your troth now, King Estmere,
  By heaven and your right hand,
That you will marry me to your wife,
  And make me queen of your land.'

Then King Estmere he plighted his troth,
  By heaven and his right hand,
That he would marry her to his wife,
  And make her queen of his land.

136

And he took his leave of that lady fair,
　To go to his own countrỳ,
To fetch him dukes, and lords, and knights,
　That they might married be.

They had not ridden scant a mile,
　A mile forth of the town,
But in came Bremor, King of Spain,
　With fighting-men many a one.

She sent a page after King Estmere,
　In all the speed might be,
That he must turn again and fight,
　Or go home and lose his ladỳ.

One while then the page he ran,
　The next while he did hurry;
Till he'd o'ertaken King Estmere,
　For no thing would he tarry.

'Tidings, tidings, King Estmere!'
　'What tidings now, my boy?'
'O tidings I can tell to you,
　That will you sore annoy.

'You had not ridden scant a mile,
　A mile out of the town,
But in came Bremor, King of Spain,
　With fighting-men many a one.

'But in came Bremor, King of Spain,
　With many a bold baròn;
One day to marry King Adland's daughter,
　The next to carry her home.

'My lady fair she greets you well,
　And evermore well by me;
You must either turn again and fight,
　Or go home and lose your ladỳ.'

Says, 'Counsel me, my brother dear,
   I'll counsel take of thee;
Whether 'tis better to turn and fight,
   Or go home and lose my ladỳ.'

'Now hearken to me,' said Adler Younge,
   'And counsel take of me;
I quickly will devise a way
   To set thy lady free.

'My mother was a western woman,
   And learned in gramarỳe,
And when I learnèd at the school,
   Something she taught it me.

'There grows a herb within this field,
   And if it were but known,
His colour which is white and red,
   It will make black and brown.

'His colour which is brown and black,
   It will make red and white;
That sword is not in all Englànd
   Upon his coat will bite.

'And you shall be a harper, brother,
   Out of the north countrỳ,
And I'll be your boy, so fain of fight,
   And bear your harp by your knee.

'And you shall be the best harper
   That ever took harp in hand,
And I will be the best singer
   That ever sung in this land.

'It shall be written in our foreheads,
   All and in grammarỳe,
That we two are the boldest men
   That are in all Christiantìe.'

And thus they arrayed themselves to ride,
   On two good harnessed steeds,
And when they came to King Adland's hall,
   Of red gold shone their weeds.

And when they came to King Adland's hall,
   Unto the fair hall gate,
There they found the proud portèr,
   Rearing himself thereat.

Says, 'Christ thee save, thou proud portèr,
   Says, 'Christ thee save and see!'
'Now you be welcome,' said the porter,
   'Of what land soever you be.'

'We be harpers,' said Adler Younge,
   'Come from the north countrỳ;
We be come hither unto this place,
   This proud wedding to see.'

Said, 'If your colour were white and red,
   As it is black and brown,
I would say King Estmere and his brother
   Were come unto this town.'

Then they pulled out a ring of gold,
   Laid it on the porter's arm;
'And ever we ask thee, proud porter,
   Thou wilt say us no harm.'

Sore he lookèd on King Estmere,
   And sore he handled the ring;
Then opened to them the fair hall gates,
   He stopped for no kind of thing.

King Estmere he stabled his steed,
   So fair at the hall-board;
The froth that came from his bridle-bit
   Lit in King Bremor's beard.

Says, 'Stable thy steed, thou proud harpèr,
 Says, 'Stable him in the stall;
It doth not beseem a proud harper's steed,
 To stable in a King's hall.'

'My lad he is so naughty,' he said,
 'He will not do what's meet;
And is there any man in this hall
 Were able him to beat?'

'Thou speaks't proud words,' said the King of Spain,
 'Thou harper here to me;
There is a man within this hall
 Will beat thy lad and thee.'

'O let that man come down,' he said,
 'A sight of him would I see!
And when he has beaten well my lad,
 Then he shall beat of me.'

Down then came a fighting-man,
 And lookèd him in the ear;
For all the gold that was under heaven,
 He durst not come him near.

'And how now, man,' said the King of Spain,
 And how, what aileth thee?'
He says, ' 'Tis writ in his forehead,
 All and in gramarỳe,
That for all the gold that is under heaven,
 I dare not venture me.'

Then King Estmere pulled forth his harp,
 And played a pretty thing.
The lady started from her seat,
 And would have gone from the king.

'Stay thy harp, thou proud harpèr,'
　For God's love I pray thee!
For if thou playest as thou hast begun,
　Thou'lt win my bride from me.'

He struck upon his harp again,
　And played a pretty thing.
The lady laughed a loud laughter,
　As she sat by the king.

Says, 'Sell me thy harp, thou proud harper,
　Thy harp and thy strings all;
And as many gold nobles thou shalt have
　As here be rings in the hall.'

'What would you do with my harp,' he said,
　'If I did sell it thee?'
'To play my wife and me a strain,
　After we married be.'

'Now sell me,' quoth he, 'thy bride so gay,
　As she sits by thy knee;
And as many gold nobles I will give
　As leaves be on a tree.'

'And what would you do with my bride so gay
　If I did sell her thee?'
'More seemly it is for a lady fair
　To marry me than thee.'

He played again both loud and shrill,
　And Adler he did sing,
'O lady, this is thy own true love,
　No harper, but a king.

'O lady, this is thy own true love,
　As plainly thou mayst see,
And I'll rid thee of that foul paynim
　Who parts thy love and thee.'

The lady looked, the lady blushed,
  And blushed, and looked again,
While Adler he hath drawn his brand,
  And hath King Bremor slain.

Up then rose the fighting men,
  And loud began to cry,
'Ah! traitors, ye have slain our king,
  And therefore ye shall die!'

King Estmere threw the harp aside,
  And swiftly drew his brand,
And Estmere he and Adler Younge
  Right stiff in fight did stand.

And aye their swords so sore did bite,
  Through help of gramarỳe,
That soon they have slain the fighting-men,
  Or forced them forth to flee.

King Estmere took that fair lady,
  And married her to his wife,
And brought her home to merry Englànd,
  With her to lead his life.

The Bonnie Banks of Fordie

There were three sisters lived in a bower,
  Eh wow bonnie,
And they went out to pull a flower,
  On the bonnie banks of Fordie.

They had not pulled a flower but one,
  Eh wow bonnie,
When up there started a banished man,
  On the bonnie banks of Fordie.

He's ta'en the first sister by the hand,
  Eh wow bonnie,
And he's turned her round and he's made her stand
  On the bonnie banks of Fordie.

'It's whether will you be a rank robber's wife,
  Eh wow bonnie,
Or will you die by my wee penknife,
  On the bonnie banks of Fordie?'

'It's I'll not be a rank robber's wife,
  Eh wow bonnie,
But I'd rather die by your wee penknife,
  On the bonnie banks of Fordie.'

He's killed this maid, and he's laid her by,
  Eh wow bonnie,
For to bear the red rose company,
  On the bonnie banks of Fordie.

He's ta'en the second one by the hand,
  Eh wow bonnie,
And he's turned her round and he's made her stand,
  On the bonnie banks of Fordie.

'It's whether will you be a rank robber's wife,
  Eh wow bonnie,
Or will you die by my wee penknife,
  On the bonnie banks of Fordie?'

'It's I'll not be a rank robber's wife,
  Eh wow bonnie,
But I'd rather die by your wee penknife,
  On the bonnie banks of Fordie.'

He's killed this maid, and he's laid her by,
  Eh wow bonnie,
For to bear the red rose company,
  On the bonnie banks of Fordie.

He's taken the youngest one by the hand,
  Eh wow bonnie,
And he's turned her round and he's made her stand,
  On the bonnie banks of Fordie.

Says, 'Will you be a rank robber's wife,
  Eh wow bonnie,
Or will you die by my wee penknife,
  On the bonnie banks of Fordie?'

'It's I'll not be a rank robber's wife,
  Eh wow bonnie,
Nor will I die by your wee penknife,
  On the bonnie banks of Fordie.

'For I have a brother beyond the sea,
  Eh wow bonnie,
And if you kill me, it's he'll kill thee,
  On the bonnie banks of Fordie.'

'Now tell me what is your brother's name,
  Eh wow bonnie?'
'My brother's name is Babylon,
  On the bonnie banks of Fordie.'

'O sister, sister, woe be to me,
  Eh wow bonnie,
O have I done this ill to thee,
  On the bonnie banks of Fordie?

'The sky shall fall on yonder green,
  Eh wow bonnie,
Or ever I shall again be seen,
  On the bonnie banks of Fordie.'

O he's pulled out his wee penknife,
  Eh wow bonnie,
And taken away his own sweet life.
  On the bonnie banks of Fordie.

Earl Mar's Daughter

It was in a pleasant time,
  Upon a summer's day,
The noble Earl Mar's daughter
  Went forth to sport and play.

And as she played and sported
  Among the lily flower,
There she spied a sprightly dove,
  Set high upon a tower.

'O Coo-me-doo, my love so true,
  If you'll come down to me,
You'll have a cage of good red gold,
  Instead of simple tree.

'I'll put gold hinges round your cage,
  And silver round your wall,
I'll make you shine as fair a bird
  As any of them all.'

But she had not these words well spoke,
  Nor yet these words well said,
Till Coo-me-doo flew from the tower
  And lighted on her head.

Then she has brought this pretty bird
  Home to her bowers and hall,
And made him shine as fair a bird
  As any of them all.

When day was gone, and night was come,
  About the evening tide,
This lady spied a gallant youth
  Stand straight up by her side.

'From whence come you, young man?' she said,
  'That does surprise me sore!
What way did you get in?' she said,
  'Fast bolted was the door.'

'O hold your tongue, ye lady fair,
  Let all your folly be!
Mind ye not of the turtle-dove
  Ye wiled from off the tree?'

'What country come ye from?' she said,
  'And what's your pedigree?'
'O it was but this very day
  That I came o'er the sea.

'My mother lives on foreign isles,
  A queen of high degree;
And by her spells I am a dove
  To live and die with thee.'

'O Coo-me-doo, my love so true,
  No more from me ye'll go?'
'That's never my intent, my love,
  As you said, it shall be so.'

Then he has stayed in bower with her
  For six long years and one,
Till six young sons to him she bare,
  And the seventh she's brought home.

But aye, as ever a child is born,
  He flies with them away,
And brings them to his mother's care,
  As fast as ever he may.

And when for seven long years and more
  He's stayed in bower with her,
There came a lord of high renown
  To court this lady fair.

But still his proffer she refused
  And all his presents too;
Says, 'I'm content to live alone
  With my bird Coo-me-doo.'

Her father swore a mighty oath,
  And Coo-me-doo it heard:
'Tomorrow, or ere I eat or drink,
  I'll kill that cursèd bird!'

Then Coo-me-doo took flight and flew
  Afar beyond the sea,
And lighted near his mother's castle,
  On a tower of gold sat he.

His mother she was walking out
  To see what she could spy,
And there she saw her one young son
  Set on a tower so high.

'Get dancers here to dance,' she said,
  'And minstrels for to play;
For here's my young son Florentine
  Come home with me to stay.'

'Get no dancers to dance, mother,
  Nor minstrels for to play;
For the mother of my seven sons,
  The morn's her wedding day.'

'O tell me, tell me, Florentine,
  Tell me, and tell me true;
Tell me this day without a flaw
  What will I do for you?'

'Instead of dancers to dance, mother,
  Or minstrels for to play,
Turn four-and-twenty lusty men
  Like storks in feathers grey:

'My seven sons in seven swans
    Above their heads to flee;
And I myself a gay goshawk,
    A bird of high degree.'

Then sighing said the Queen herself,
    'That thing's too high for me!'
But she applied to an old woman
    Who had more skill than she.

Instead of dancers to dance a dance,
    Or minstrels for to play,
Four-and-twenty lusty men
    Turned birds of feathers grey.

The seven sons in seven swans
    Above their heads to flee,
And he himself a gay goshawk,
    A bird of high degree.

This flock of birds took flight and flew
    Beyond the raging sea;
And landed near Earl Mar's castle,
    Took shelter in every tree.

They were a flock of pretty birds,
    Right comely to be seen;
The people viewed them with surprise,
    As they dancèd on the green.

These birds flew out from every tree,
    And lighted on the hall,
And from the roof with force did flee
    Among the nobles all.

The storks then seized the wedding guests,
    They could not fight nor flee;
The swans they bound the bridegroom fast
    Below a green oak tree.

They lighted next on the bridesmaidens,
  Then on the bride's own head,
And with the twinkling of an eye
  The bride and them were fled.

There's ancient men at weddings been
  For sixty years or more,
But such a curious wedding day,
  They've never seen before.

For nothing could the company do,
  Nor nothing could they say;
But they saw a flock of pretty birds
  That took their bride away.

King Orpheo

There lived a king into the east,
There lived a lady in the west.

This king he has a-hunting gone,
He's left his lady Isabel alone.

'O why had you away to go?
Now at your home is grief and woe.

'For the King of Faerie with his dart
Has pierced your lady to the heart.'

And after them the king has gone,
But when he came it was a grey stone.

Then he took out his pipes and played,
But his heart was sore dismayed.

And first he played the notes of annoy,
And then he played the notes of joy,

And then he played the good gay reel
That might a sick heart make to heal.

'Now come you into our hall,
And come you in among us all.'

Now he's gone into their hall,
And he's gone in among them all.

Then he took out his pipes and played,
But his heart was sore dismayed.

And first he played the notes of annoy,
And then he played the notes of joy.

And then he played the good gay reel,
That might a sick heart make to heal.

'Now tell to us what is your pay,
What shall we give you for your play?'

'What is my pay I will you tell,
And that's my lady Isabel.'

'You'll take your lady and you'll go home,
And you'll be king over all your own.'

He's ta'en his lady and he's gone home,
And now he's king over all his own.

Brown Adam

O who would wish the wind to blow
  Or the green leaves fall therewith?
Or who would wish a more loyal love
  Than Brown Adam the Smith?

But they have banished Brown Adam
  From father and from mother;
And they have banished Brown Adam
  From sister and from brother;

And they have banished Brown Adam
  From the flower of all his kin;
And he's built a bower in the good green-wood
  Between his lady and him.

Brown Adam has taken his sword in hand,
  And his bow his arm upon,
And he is forth in the good green-wood
  To hunt some venison.

O he's shot up and he's shot down
  The bunting in the briar,
And he's sent it home to his ladỳ,
  Bade her be of good cheer.

O he's shot up and he's shot down
  The linnet on the thorn,
And sent it home to his ladỳ,
  Said he'd be home at morn.

When he came to his lady's bower-door,
  A little thereby stood he,
And there he heard a full false knight
  Tempting his gay ladỳ.

This knight's ta'en out a gay gold ring,
   Had cost him many a crown,
'O grant me love for love, ladỳ,
   And this shall be your own.'

'I love Brown Adam well,' she says,
   'I wot so he does me;
I would not give Brown Adam's love
   For no false knight I see.'

Out he has ta'en a purse of gold,
   Was all full to the string;
'O grant me love for love, ladỳ,
   And take this offerìng.'

'I love Brown Adam well,' she says,
   'And I know so does he me;
And I would not be your light-of-love
   For more than you'd give me.'

Then out he drew his long, long brand,
  And flashed it in her face;
'Now grant me love for love, ladỳ,
  Or through you this shall pierce.'

'O,' sighing said that gay ladỳ,
  'Brown Adam tarries long!'
Then up and starts him Brown Adam,
  Says, 'Lady, fear no wrong.'

He's made him leave his bow, his bow,
  He's made him leave his brand;
He's made him leave a better pledge—
  Four fingers of his right hand.

Adam Bell,
Clym of the Clough,
and William of Cloudesley

THE FIRST FYTTE

Merry it was in the green forèst,
  Among the leaves so green,
Where that men walk east and west
  With bows and arrows keen,

To raise the deer out of their den;
  Such sights have oft been seen,
As by three yeomen of the north countrỳ,
  By them it is I mean.

The one of them was Adam Bell,
  The other Clym of the Clough,
The third was William of Cloudèsley,
  An archer good enough.

They were outlawed for venison,
  These yeomen every one,
They swore them brethren upon a day
  And to Ingle Wood are gone.

Now listen, all ye gentlemen,
  That of mirth love to hear,
Two of them were single men,
  The third had a wife so dear.

William was the wedded man,
  Much more then was his care,
He said to his brethren upon a day,
  To Carlisle would he fare,

For to speak with Alice his wife,
  And with his children three.
'By my troth,' said Adam Bell,
  'Not by the counsel of me!

'For if you go to Carlisle, brother,
  And from this wild wood wend.
If the Justice may you take,
  Your life were at an end.'

'If that I come not tomorrow, brother,
  By prime to you again,
Trust not else but that I'm taken,
  Or else that I am slain.'

He took his leave of his brethren two,
  And to Carlisle he is gone;
There he knocked at his own window,
  Shortly and anon.

'Where be you, fair Alice,' he said,
  'My wife and children three?
Lightly let in thine own husband,
  William of Cloudèsley.'

'Alas, alas!' said fair Alice,
  And she sighed wondrous sore;
'This place has been beset for you
  A whole half year and more!'

'Now I am here,' said Cloudèsley,
  'I would that in I were;
Now fetch us meat and drink enough,
  And let us make good cheer.'

She fetched him meat and drink plentỳ,
  Like a true wedded wife,
And pleased him with all that she had.
  Whom she loved as her life.

There lay an old wife in that place,
    A little beside the fire,
William had kept her in charity
    More than seven year;

Up she rose, and forth she goes—
    Evil may she speed therefore!—
For she had set no foot on ground
    In seven years before.

She went into the Justice Hall
    As fast as ever could be:
'This night,' she said, 'is come to town
    William of Cloudèsley.'

159

Thereof the Justice was full glad,
    And so was the Sheriff alsò,
'Thou shalt not come hither, dame, for nought
    Thy reward shalt thou have, ere thou go.'

They gave to her, as I've heard tell,
    A right good scarlet gown;
She took the gift and home she went,
    And softly couched her down.

They raised the town of merry Carlisle,
    In all the haste they can,
And they came thronging to William's house,
    As fast as they could run.

There they beset that good yeomàn,
    About on every side;
William heard great noise of folks,
    That thither-ward fast hied.

Alice opened a little window,
    And lookèd all about,
She was ware of the Justice and Sheriff both,
    With a full great rout.

'Alas, treason!' cried fair Alice.
    'Ever woe may you be!
Go into my chamber, my husband,' she said,
    'Sweet William of Cloudèsley.'

He took his sword and his bucklèr,
    His bow and his children three,
And went into his strongest chamber
    Where he thought safest to be.

Fair Alice, like a lover true,
    Took a pole-axe in her hand,
Said, 'He shall die that cometh in
    This door while I may stand!'

Cloudèsley bent a well good bow,
    It was of trusty tree,
He smote the Justice on the breast,
    That his arrow burst in three.

'God's curse on his heart,' said William then,
    'This day that thy coat put on!
If it had been no better than mine,
    It had gone near thy bone.'

'Yield thee, Cloudesley,' said the Justice,
    'Cast down thine arrows and bow.'
'God's curse on his heart!' said fair Alice,
    'That my husband counselleth so!'

'Set fire on the house,' then said the Sheriff,
    'Since it will no better be;
And burn we therein William,' he said,
    'His wife and his children three!'

They fired the house in many a place,
    The fire flew up on high.
'Alas, alas!' cried fair Alice,
    'I see we here shall die!'

William opened a back window,
    Set in his chamber wall,
And there with sheets he did let down,
    His wife and children small.

'Have here my treasure,' said William then,
    'My wife and children three;
For Christ His sake do them no harm,
    But wreak you all on me.'

Till his arrows all were gone,
    William shot wondrous well,
The fire his bowstring burnt in two,
    So fast on him it fell.

The sparkles burnt and fell upon
  Good William of Cloudèsley:
'This way to burn,' says that woeful man,
  'Is a coward's death to me.

'Rather I would,' said bold Williàm,
  'With my sword in the rout to run,
Than here among my enemies' wood,
  Thus cruelly to burn.'

He took his sword and his buckler then,
  And among them all he ran;
Where the people were most in press,
  He shot down many a man.

There might no man abide his stroke,
  So fiercely on them he ran;
Then they threw windows and doors on him,
  And so took that good yeomàn.

There they bound him hand and foot,
  And in a deep dungeon him cast.
'Now Cloudesley,' said the high Justìce,
  'Thou shalt be hanged at last.'

'I vow I shall make for thee,' said the Sheriff,
  'A pair of gallows new,
And Carlisle gates shall all be shut,
  And no man shall come through.

'Then shall not help thee Clym of the Clough,
  Nor yet shall Adam Bell,
Though they came with a thousand more,
  Nor all the devils in hell.'

Early in the morning the Justice uprose,
  To the gates first is he gone,
And commanded to shut close
  Lightly every one.

Then went he to the market-place,
　　As fast as ever could be,
A pair of new gallows there he set up,
　　Beside the pillorỳ.

A little boy among them asked,
　　'What meaneth that gallows-tree?'
They said, 'To hang a good yeomàn,
　　William of Cloudèsley.'

This little boy was the town swineherd,
　　And kept fair Alice's swine;
Oft he'd seen William in the wood,
　　Who'd given him there to dine.

He went out at a crevice in the wall,
　　And light to the wood is gone;
There he met those bold yeomèn,
　　Shortly and anon.

'Alas!' then said that little boy,
　　'Ye tarry here all too long;
Cloudesley is taken and doomed to death,
　　And ready for to hang.'

'Alas!' then said good Adam Bell,
　　'That ever we see this day!
He might here have with us dwelled,
　　So oft we did him pray.

'He might have tarried in green forèst,
　　Under the green shadòws,
And have kept both us and him at rest,
　　Out of all troubles and woes.'

Adam bent a right good bow,
　　A great hart soon has he slain:
'Take that to thy dinner, child,' he said,
　　'And bring me mine arrow again.'

'Now go we hence,' said these stout yeomèn,
  'We tarry no longer here;
We shall rescue him, by God's grace,
  Though we should pay full dear.'

To Carlisle went these good yeomen,
  On a merry morning of May.
Here is a Fytte of Cloudèsley,
  Another is for to say.

THE SECOND FYTTE

And when they came to merry Carlisle,
  All in a morning tide,
They found the gates against them shut,
  Round on every side.

'Alas!' then said good Adam Bell,
  'That ever we were made men!
These gates be shut so wonderly well,
  We may not come here in.'

Then up and spake him Clym of the Clough,
  'With a wile we will in us bring.
Let us say we be messengers,
  Having straight come from our King.'

Said Adam, 'I have a letter written,
  Now let us wisely work,
We will say we have the King his seal,
  I hold the porter no clerk.'

Then Adam Bell beat on the gate,
  With strokes full great and strong;
The porter heard such noise thereat,
  And to the gate he throng.

'Who is there now?' said the porter,
  'That maketh all this knocking?'
'We be two messengers,' said Clym of the Clough,
  'Be come right from our King.'

'We have a letter,' said Adam Bell,
  'To the Justice we must it bring;
Let us in our message to do,
  That we go again to our King.'

'Here cometh no man in,' said the porter,
  'By Him that died on a tree,
Till that a false thief be hanged,
  Called William of Cloudèsley.'

Then spoke the yeoman, Clym of the Clough
  And swore by Mary free,
'If that we stand here long without,
  Like a thief hanged thou shalt be!

'Lo, here we have the King his seal,
  What, blockhead, art thou mad?'
The porter thought it had been so,
  And lightly did off his hood.

'Welcome is my lord's seal,' he said,
  'For that ye shall come in.'
Right shortly then he opened the gate
  —An evil opening for him!

'Now we are in,' said Adam Bell,
  'Thereof we are full fain,
But Christ He knows, who harrowed hell,
  How we'll come out again.'

'Had we the keys,' said Clym of the Clough,
  'Right well then should we speed;
Then we might come out well enough,
  When we see time and need.'

They called the porter to speak with them,
  And wrung his neck with ease,
Then cast him into a deep dungeon,
  And took from him the keys.

'Now I am porter,' said Adam Bell,
  'See, brother, the keys have we here;
The worst porter to merry Carlisle
  They have had this hundred year!

'And now we will our good bows bend,
  Into the town will we go,
For to deliver our dear brother,
  That lies in care and woe.'

Then each one bent his good yew bow,
  And looked their strings were round;
To the market place of merry Carlisle
  They came with little sound.

And as they looked them all about,
  A pair of new gallows they see;
And the Justice with a jury of squires,
  That judged William hanged to be.

And Cloudesley lay ready there in a cart,
  Fast bound both foot and hand,
And a strong rope about his neck,
  All ready to be hanged.

The Justice called to him a lad,
  Cloudesley's clothes should he have,
To take the measure of that yeomàn,
  Thereafter to make his grave.

'I have seen as great marvel,' said Cloudèsley,
  'As between this and prime,
He that maketh this grave for me,
  Himself may lie therein.'

'Thou speakest proudly,' then said the Justice,
  'I shall hang thee with my hand!'
Full well that heard his brethren two,
  There still as they did stand.

Then Cloudesley cast his eyes aside,
  And saw his brethren stand
At the corner of the market place,
  With their good bows bent in their hand.

'I see comfort,' said Cloudèsley,
  'Yet hope I well to fare;
If I might have my hands at will,
  Right little would I care.'

Then bespake good Adam Bell,
  To Clym of the Clough so free,
'Brother, mark you the Justice well,
  Lo! yonder you may him see;

'And at the Sheriff shoot I will,
  Strongly with arrow keen.'
—A better shot in merry Carlisle
  This seven year was not seen.

They loosed their arrows both at once,
  Of no man had they dread,
The one hit the Justice, the other the Sheriff,
  That both full sorely bled.

All men fled that stood them nigh
  When the Justice fell to the ground,
And the Sheriff fell close by,
  Either had his death's wound.

All the citizens fast did fly,
  They durst no longer abide;
Then lightly loosed they Cloudèsley,
  Where he with ropes lay tied.

William leaped to a constable,
  And wrung the axe from his hand,
On either side he smote them down,
  Not one could him withstand.

'This day let us live together,' said William,
  'Or die, if it chance may be!
And if e'er you have need, as I have now,
  The same you shall find by me.'

They fought together as brethren true,
  Like hardy men and bold;
Many a man to the ground they threw,
  And many a heart made cold.

But when their arrows were all gone,
   Men pressed to them full fast;
Then they drew their swords anon,
   And their bows from them did cast.

They went lightly on their way,
   With swords and bucklers round;
By the middle of the day,
   They had made many a wound.

There was many a neat-horn in Carlisle blown,
   And the bells backward did ring;
Many a woman said, 'Alas!'
   And many their hands did wring.

The Mayor of Carlisle was come forth,
   And with him a full great rout;
These three yeomen dread him full sore,
   For their lives stood now in doubt.

The Mayor came armed at a full great pace,
   With a pole-axe in his hand,
Many a strong man with him was,
   In that press of fight to stand.

The Mayor smote Cloudesley with his bill,
   His buckler he burst in two;
'Keep we the gates fast shut,' he bade,
   'That these traitors thereout not go.'

But all for nought was that they wrought,
   So fast they fell to ground,
Till they all three that so manfully fought,
   Were gotten without at a bound.

'Have here your keys,' said Adam Bell,
   'Mine office I here forsake,
If you will do by my counsel,
   A new porter you will make!'

He threw the keys there at their heads,
    And bade them evil to thrive,
And all who prevent any good yeomàn
    To come and comfort his wife.

Thus be these good yeomen gone to the wood,
    As light as leaf on tree;
They laugh and be merry in their mood,
    No enemy now could they see.

When they came to Ingle Wood,
    Under their trysting tree,
There they found many bows full good,
    And of arrows great plentỳ.

'So help me God,' said Adam Bell,
    And Clym of the Clough so free,
'I would we were now in merry Carlisle,
    Before that fair companỳ!'

They sit them down and make good cheer,
    And eat and drink full well.
—Here's a second Fytte of these bold yeomèn,
    And another I shall you tell.

THE THIRD FYTTE

As they sat in Ingle Wood,
    Under their trysting tree,
They thought they heard a woman weep,
    But her they might not see.

Sore there sighed the fair Alìce,
    'That e'er I see this day!
For now is my dear husband slain,
    Alas! and well-away!

'Might I have spoken with his brethren,
    With either of them twain,
To show them what to him befell,
    My heart were out of pain.'

Cloudesley walked a little beside,
    Looked under the green-wood tree,
And there full woe in heart and mind,
    Saw wife and children three.

'Welcome, wife,' then said William,
    'Under this trysting tree!
I had thought yestreen, by sweet Saint John,
    Thou shouldst me never more see.'

'Now well is me!' said fair Alìce,
    'My heart is out of woe!'
'Dame,' he said, 'be merry and glad,
    And thank my brethren two.'

'Hereof to speak,' said Adam Bell,
    'I think it is no boot;
The meat that we must sup withal,
    It runs still fast on foot.'

Then went they down into a glade,
    These noble archers all three,
Each of them shot a hart of grease,
    The best that they could see.

'Have here the best, Alice my wife,'
    Said William of Cloudèsley,
'Because when I was slain full nigh,
    You boldly stood by me.'

And then they went to their suppèr,
    With such meat as they had,
And thanked God of their good fortune,
    And were both merry and glad

And when that they had supped full well,
   Certain on hart of grease,
Cloudesley said, 'We will to our King,
   To get us a charter of peace.

'Alice shall be at sojourning
   In a nunnery here beside,
My two sons shall with her go,
   And there they shall abide.

'My eldest son shall go with me,
   For him I have no care,
And he shall bring Alice word again,
   How that we do fare.'

Then fast they have to London gone,
   These brave yeomen all three,
Till they came to the King's palàce,
   Where they had need to be.

And when they came to the King his court,
   Unto the palace gate,
Of no man would they ask no leave,
   But boldly went in thereat.

They pressèd quickly into the hall,
   Of no man had they dread,
The porter came after and did them call,
   And them began to chide.

The usher said, 'Yeomen, what would ye have?
   I pray you tell to me.
By this you might make officers blamed,
   Good sirs, of whence be ye?'

'Sir, we be outlaws of the forest,
   Certain, without lyìng,
And hither to get us a charter of peace,
   We come unto our King.'

And when they came before our King,
    As it was the law of the land,
They all kneeled down without delay,
    And each held up his hand.

They said, 'Lord, we beseech thee here,
    That ye will grant us grace,
For we have slain your fat fallow deer,
    In many a sundry place.'

'What be your names?' then said our King,
    'Anon that you tell me.'
They said, 'Adam Bell, Clym of the Clough,
    And William of Cloudèsley.'

'Be ye those thieves,' then said our King,
    'That men have told of to me?
Here to God I make a vow
    Ye shall be hanged all three!

'Ye shall be dead without mercỳ,
    As I am King of this land!'
He commanded his officers every one
    Fast on them to lay hand.

There they took these good yeomen,
    And arrested them all three.
'So may I thrive,' said Adam Bell,
    'This game liketh not me!

'But, good my lord, we beseech you now,
    That you will grant us grace,
Insomuch as we be to you come,
    Or else that we may from you pace,

'With such weapons as we have here,
    Till we be out of your place.
And if we live this hundred year,
    Of you we will ask no grace.'

'Ye speak proudly,' said our King,
  'Ye shall be hanged all three.'
'That were great pity,' then said the Queen,
  'If any grace might be.

'My lord, when I came first to this land,
  Your wedded wife to be,
You said that the first boon I should ask,
  You would grant it speedilỳ.

'And I asked you never none till now,
  Therefore, lord, grant it me!'
'Now ask it, madam,' said the King,
  'And granted it shall be.'

'Then good my lord, I you beseech,
  These yeomen grant ye me.'
'Madam, you might have asked a boon
  That should have been worth them three.

'You might have asked for towers and towns,
  Parks and forests plentỳ.'
'None so pleasant to my heart,' she said,
  'Nor none so dear to me.'

'Madam, since it is your desire,
  Your asking granted shall be.
But I had rather have given you
  Market towns more than three.'

The Queen she was a glad womàn,
  And said, 'Lord, gramercỳ!
I dare well undertake for them
  That true men shall they be.

'But good lord, speak some merry word,
  That comfort they may see.'
'I grant you grace,' then said our King,
  'Wash, fellows, and to meat go ye.'

174

They had not sat but a little while,
    Certain without lying,
When came two messengers out of the north,
    With letters to our King.

And when they came before the King,
    They kneeled down on their knee,
Said, 'Lord, your officers greet you well,
    Of Carlisle in the north country.'

'How fares my Justice?' said the King,
    'How fares my Sheriff also?'
'Sir, they be slain without lying,
    And many a man laid low.'

'Who hath them slain?' then said the King,
    'Anon thou tell to me.'
'Sir, Adam Bell, and Clym of the Clough,
    And William of Cloudesley.'

'Alas, for ruth!' then said our King,
    'My heart is wondrous sore;
I had rather than a thousand pound
    I had known of this before;

'For I have granted to them grace,
    And that repenteth me;
But had I known all this before,
    They had been hanged all three.'

The King he opened the letter anon,
    Himself he read it then,
And found how these outlaws had slain
    More than three hundred men:

First the Justice and the Sheriff,
    And the Mayor of Carlisle town,
Of constables and catchipolls,
    Alive were scant left one.

The bailiffs and the beadles both
　　The sergeants of law alsò,
And forty of the forest keepers,
　　These outlaws had laid low.

And broken his parks, and slain his deer;
　　Over all they chose the best,
So perilous outlaws as they were
　　Walked not by east nor west.

When the King this letter had read,
　　In his heart he sighed full sore.
'Take up the tables,' anon he bade,
　　'For I may eat no more.'

The King called to his best archers,
　　To the butts with him to go;
'I will see these fellows shoot,' he said,
　　'In the north have wrought this woe.'

The King's bowmen made ready straightway,
　　And the Queen's archers alsò,
So did these three bold yeomèn,
　　With them they thought to go.

There twice or thrice they shot about,
　　For to assay their hand;
There was no shot these yeomen shot,
　　That any mark might stand.

Then spake him William of Cloudèsley,
　　'By Him that for me died,
I hold him never no good archer,
　　That shooteth at butts so wide.'

'Whereat would you shoot then?' said our King.
　　'I pray thee tell to me.'
'At such a butt, sir,' William said,
　　'As men use in my countrỳ.'

William went into the field,
    And with him his two brethrèn,
There they set up two hazel rods,
    Twenty score paces between.

'I hold him an archer,' said Cloudèsley,
    'That yonder wand cleaveth in two.'
'Here is none such,' said the King,
    'For no man can that do.'

'I shall assay, sir,' said Cloudèsley,
    'Ere that I farther go.'
Cloudesley with a long arrow,
    Clave the wand in two.

'Thou art the best archer,' said the King,
    'Forsooth that ever I see.'
'And yet for your love,' said William,
    'I will do more masterỳ.'

'I have a son is seven years old,
    He is to me full dear,
I will tie him to a stake,
    All shall see that be here.

'And lay an apple upon his head,
    And six score paces go,
And I myself with a broad arrow,
    Shall cleave the apple in two.'

'Now haste thee, haste thee,' said the King,
    'By Him that died on a tree!
But if thou do not as thou hast said,
    Hangèd thou shalt be.

'If thou touch his head or gown,
    In sight that men may see,
By all the saints that be in heaven,
    I shall you hang all three.'

'What I have promised,' said Cloudèsley,
  'That I will never forsake.'
And there, even before the King,
  In the earth he drove a stake.

And bound thereto his eldest son,
  And bade him stand still thereat,
And turned the child's face away from him,
  Because he should not start.

An apple upon his head he set,
  And then his bow he bent.
Six score paces they measured out,
  And thither Cloudesley went.

There he drew out a fair broad arrow
  (His bow was great and long)
He set that arrow to his bow,
  That was both stiff and strong.

He prayed the people that was there,
  That they all still would stand,
'For he that shooteth for such a wager,
  Behoveth a steadfast hand.'

Much people prayed for Cloudèsley,
  That his life saved might be;
And when he made him ready to shoot,
  Was many a weeping e'e.

But Cloudesley cleft the apple in two,
  As many a man might see.
'Now God forbid,' then said our King,
  'That ever thou shoot at me!

'I give thee eighteen pence a day,
  And my bow shalt thou bear,
And over all the north countrỳ,
  I make thee chief rangèr.'

'And I will add to that,' said the Queen,
  'Seventeen pence a day.
Come fetch thy payment when thou wilt,
  No man shall say thee nay.

'William, I make thee a gentleman
  Of clothing and of fee,
And thy brethren yeomen of my chamber,
  For they are seemly to see.

'Your son, for he is tender of age,
  Of my wine cellar shall he be,
And when he cometh to man's estate,
  Better preferred shall he be.

'And William, bring me your wife,' said the Queen,
  'Me longeth her sore to see;
She shall be chief gentlewoman,
  To govern my nursery.'

The yeomen thanked them all courteously,
   And said, 'To Rome will we wend,
Of all the sins that we have done
   To be absolved at his hand.'

So forth be gone these good yeomèn,
   As fast as ever might be;
And after came and dwelt with the King,
   And died good men all three.

Thus ended the lives of these good yeomèn,
   God send them eternal bliss;
And all that with a hand-bow shooteth,
   That of heaven they may never miss!

The Elfin-knight

My plaid away, my plaid away,
And o'er the hills and far away,
And far away to Norroway,
My plaid shall not be blown away!

Lady Isabel sits in her bower sewing,
  Aye as the daisies grow gay,
She heard an elf-knight his horn a-blowing,
  The first morning in May.

The elfin-knight sits on yon hill,
He blows his horn both loud and shrill,
He blows it east, he blows it west,
He blows it where he liketh best.

'I wish that horn were in my chest,
Yea, and the knight in my arms next.'
These words no sooner said had she,
When the knight stood at her knee.

'Thou art o'er young a maid,' quoth he,
'Married with me thou ill would'st be.'
'I have a sister younger than I,
And she was married yesterday.'

'Married with me if thou wouldst be,
A courtesy thou must do to me.
For thou must make a shirt for me,
Without any cut or hem,' quoth he.

'It's you must shape it knife-and-shearless,
And also sew it needle-threadless.
And you must wash it in yonder well,
Where the dew never wet nor the rain never fell,
And you must dry it upon a thorn
That never budded since Adam was born.'

'Now since you've asked some things of me,
It's right I should ask as many of thee.
My father he gave me an acre of land,
Between the salt sea and the strand.

'And you must plough it with your blowing horn,
And you must sow it with peppercorn,
And you must harrow it with one prong,
And you must shear it with one horse-bone.

'And you must stack it in yon mouse-hole,
And you must thresh it in your shoe-sole.
And you must bring it over the sea,
Fair and clean and dry to me.
And when you've done and finished your work,
Come to me, love, and get your shirt.'

'It's I'll not quit my plaid for my life,
It wraps my seven bairns and my wife.'
 The wind shall not blow my plaid away.
'And it's I will keep me a maiden still,
Let the elfin-knight do what he will.'
 The wind shall not blow my plaid away.

The Gay Goshawk

'O well is me, my gay goshawk,
  That ye can speak and flee;
For you shall carry a love-letter
  To my true-love from me.'

'O how shall I your true-love find,
  Or how should I her know?
When from her mouth I ne'er heard speech,
  Nor with mine eyes her saw.'

'O well shall you my true-love know,
  As soon as her you see;
For of all the flowers in fair England,
  The fairest flower is she.

183

'And when you come to her castle,
  Light on the bush of ash,
And sit ye there, and sing ye there,
  As she comes from the mass.

'And when she goes into the house,
  Light ye upon the whin,
And sit ye there, and sing ye there,
  As she goes out and in.'

Lord William has written a love-letter
  Put it under the wing so grey,
And fast and fast as he can fly
  The goshawk is away.

And when he came to that castle,
  He lighted on the ash,
And there he sat, and there he sang,
  As she came from the mass.

And when she went into the house,
  He flew unto the whin;
And there he sat, and there he sang,
  As she went out and in.

'O eat and drink my maidens all,
  The wine flows you among,
Whilst I go to the west-window,
  And hear yon bonny bird's song.'

O first he sang a merry song,
  And then he sang a grave,
And then he pecked his feathers grey,
  To her the letter gave.

'You're bidden send your love a send,
  For he has sent you five,
And tell him where you'll meet with him,
  If you'd find him alive.'

'I send him the rings from my white fingers,
  The garlands off my hair,
I send him the heart that's in my breast,
  What would my love have mair?
And at the fourth kirk in fair Scotland,
  Ye'll bid him meet me there.'

She's gone unto her father dear,
  Knelt low down on her knee,
'A boon, a boon, my father dear,
  I pray you grant it me!'

'Ask on, ask on, my daughter dear,
  And granted it shall be;
Except one squire in fair Scotland,
  And him you shall never see.'

'The only boon, my father dear,
  That I do crave of thee,
Is, if I die in southern lands,
  In Scotland to bury me.

'At the first kirk in fair Scotland,
  You'll cause the bells be rung;
At the next kirk in fair Scotland,
  You'll cause the mass be sung;

At the third kirk in fair Scotland,
  You'll deal the gold for me;
At the fourth kirk in fair Scotland,
  It's there you'll bury me.'

She's gone unto her pleasant bower,
  As fast as she could fare;
And she has taken a sleepy draught
  That she had mixed with care.

She's laid her down upon her bed,
    And soon she's fallen asleep,
And soon o'er every tender limb
    Cold death began to creep.

When night was flown, and day was come,
    Not one that did her see
But thought she was as surely dead
    As any lady could be.

Her father and her brothers dear
    Have made for her a bier,
The one half was of good red gold,
    The other of silver clear.

Her mother and her sisters fair
    Have made for her a pall,
The one half was of satin fine,
    The other embroidered all.

The first Scots kirk that they came to,
    They caused the bells be rung;
The next Scots kirk that they came to,
    They caused the mass be sung;

The third Scots kirk that they came to,
    They dealt the gold for her;
The fourth Scots kirk that they came to,
    Her true-love met them there.

'Set down, set down the bier,' he says,
    Till I look on the dead;
The last time that I saw her face,
    Her cheeks were rosy red.'

He rent the sheet from off her face,
    A little above the chin;
And fast he saw her colour come,
    And sweet she smiled on him.

'O give me a slice of your bread, my love,
  And one cup of your wine;
For I have fasted for your sake,
  These weary long days nine.

'Go home, go home, my seven bold brothers,
  Go home and blow your horn,
And ye may boast in southern lands
  Your sister played you scorn!

'I came not here to fair Scotland
  To lie among the dead;
But I came here to fair Scotland,
  With my true-love to wed.'

The Demon Lover

'O where have you been, my long-lost love,
  These long seven years and more?'
'O I'm come to seek my former vows,
  That you promised me before.'

'O hold your tongue of your former vows,
  For they'll breed bitter strife,
O hold your tongue of your former vows,
  For I am become a wife.'

He turned him right and round about,
  And the tear blinded his e'e:
'I would never have trodden on Irish ground
  If it had not been for thee.

'I might have had a noble lady,
  Far, far beyond the sea,
I might have had a noble lady,
  Were it not for the love of thee.'

'If you might have had a noble lady,
  Yourself you have to blame;
You should have taken the noble lady,
  For you knew that I was none.'

'O false are the vows of womenkind,
  But fair is their false bodỳ:
I would never have trodden on Irish ground,
  Were it not for the love of thee.'

'O what have you to take me to,
  If I with you should go,
If I were to leave my good husband,
  My little young son alsò?'

'I have seven ships upon the sea,
  The eighth brought me to land,
With mariners and merchandise,
  And music on every hand.

'The ship wherein my love shall sail,
  Is glorious to behold,
The sails are of the finest silk,
  And the masts of beaten gold.'

She's taken up her little young son,
  Kissed him both cheek and chin.
'O fare you well, my little young son,
  For I'll ne'er see you again!'

They had not sailed a league, a league,
  A league but barely one,
Till she minded on her good husband,
  And on her little young son.

'O if I were at home again,
    At home where I would be,
No living man should flatter me,
    To sail upon the sea!'

'O hold your tongue of weeping,' he says,
    'Let all your follies a-be;
I'll show you where the lilies grow
    On the banks of Italy.'

They had not sailed a league, a league,
    A league but barely three,
Till grim, grim grew his countenance,
    And gurly grew the sea.

'O what hills are yon, yon pleasant hills,
    That the sun shines sweetly on?'
'O yon are the hills of Heaven,' he says,
    'Where you will never win.'

'And O what mountain is yon?' she said,
    'So dreary with frost and snow?'
'Yon is the mountain of Hell,' he said,
    Where you and I must go.

'But hold your tongue, my dearest dear,
    Let all your follies a-be;
I'll show you where the lilies grow
    At the bottom of the sea.'

And aye as she turned her round about,
    Aye taller he seemed to be,
Until the tops of that gallant ship
    No taller were than he.

He struck the top-mast with his hand,
    The fore-mast with his knee:
And he brake that gallant ship in twain,
    And sunk her in the sea.

Hynd Etin

May Margaret sits in her bower door,
    Sewing her silken seam,
She heard a note in Elmond's wood,
    And wished she there had been.

She let the seam fall to her side,
    The needle to her toe,
And she's away to Elmond's wood,
    As fast as she can go.

Then up and started Hynd Etin,
    From the shadow where he lay;
'O seek ye flowers, or seek ye dew,
    This bonny night of May?

'You're welcome to the wood, Marg'ret,
    You're welcome here to me,
A fairer bower than ever you saw,
    I'll build this night for thee.'

He has built a bower beside the thorn,
    He has fenced it up with stone,
And there within the Elmond wood
    They two have dwelt their lone.

He's kept her in the Elmond wood
    For six long years and one,
Till six pretty sons to him she bore,
    And the seventh she's brought home.

O it fell out upon a day,
    He's to the hunting gone,
And all for to carry his game for him
    He's taken his eldest son.

When they were in the gay green-wood,
    They heard the thrush to sing;
When they were up above the hill,
    They heard the kirk bells ring.

'A question I will ask, father,
    If you would not angry be?'
'Say on, say on, my bonny boy,
    You'll not be quarrelled by me.'

'I see my mother's cheeks aye wet,
    I ne'er can see them dry,
What is it makes my mother dear
    To sob so bitterly?'

'No wonder she should sob, my boy,
    No wonder she should pine,
For it is seven long year and more
    She's not seen kith nor kin,
And it is seven long years and more
    Since she to church has been.

'Your mother was a King's daughter,
    And came of high degree,
She might have wed some worthy prince,
    Had she not been stolen by me.

'For I was but her father's page,
    And served him on my knee;
And yet my love was great for her,
    And so was hers for me.

'But we'll shoot the bunting of the bush,
    The linnet of the tree,
And ye'll take them home to your dear mother,
    See if she'll merrier be.'

193

It fell upon another day,
    Hynd Etin to hunt has gone,
And all to comfort his mother dear,
    He's left his eldest son.

'O I will tell to you, mother,
    If you will not angry be?'
'Say on, say on, my bonny boy,
    Ye'll ne'er be quarrelled by me."

'As we went to the hind-hunting,
    I heard the kirk bells ring;
And O but they rang bonnily,
    Beyond all other thing.'

'My blessings on your heart, my boy,
    O were I there alone!
I have not been in holy kirk
    Since seven long years are gone.

'O it's there my father and mother are,
    And it's there that I would be,
For I am the mother of seven fair sons
    That ne'er got Christiantie.

'O come ye hither, my eldest son,
    And hearken well to me;
You'll go now down by yonder road,
    Till you pass the green-wood tree,
And when you come to the open land
    A gay castle you'll see.

'I'll follow after my brave young son,
    And bring the bairns with me,
But you go forward to the gate,
    And take these rings with thee.

'You'll give the first to the proud porter,
    And he will let you in;
You'll give the next to the butler-boy,
    And he'll show you within;

'You'll give the third to the proud harper
    That harps in the King's hall,
And he'll play success to the little wee boy,
    Standing before them all.'

He gave the first to the proud porter,
    And he opened and let him in;
He gave the next to the butler-boy,
    And he showed him within;

He gave the third to the proud harper,
    Was harping in the hall,
And he played success to the little wee boy,
    Stood there before them all.

Now when he came before the King,
    He fell low on his knee,
The King he turned him round about,
    And the tears blinded his e'e.

'Rise up, rise up, my bonny boy,
    Go from my companỳ,
You look so like my dear daughter,
    My heart will burst in three!'

'If I look like your dear daughter,
    A wonder it is none;
If I look like your dear daughter,
    I am her eldest son.'

'Now tell me, tell me, ye little wee boy,
    Where is my May Marg'ret?'
'With my six brothers even now
    She's standing at your gate.'

'O where are all my porter-boys,
    That I pay meat and fee,
To open my gates both wide and broad,
    Let her come in to me?'

When she came in before the King,
    She fell low on her knee,
'Rise up, rise up, my daughter dear,
    This day ye'll dine with me.'

'One bite I cannot eat, father,
    Nor one drop can I drink,
Until I see my dear husband,
    So long for him I think.'

'O where are all my rangers good,
    That I pay meat and fee,
To search the forest far and wide,
    And bring Hynd Etin to me?'

Out it speaks the little wee boy,
    'No, no, this must not be;
Without you grant a free pardon,
    I hope you'll ne'er him see.'

'O here I grant a free pardon,
    Well sealed by my own hand.
Go search, go search for Young Etin,
    Go search through all my land!'

They searched the country wide and broad,
    The forests far and near;
And they found him into Elmond's wood,
    Tearing his yellow hair.

'Rise up, rise up now, Hynd Etin,
    Rise up and come with me.
We're messengers from the King's court,
    The King wants you to see.'

'O let them take from me my head,
    Or hang me on a tree,
For since I've lost my dear lady,
    My life's worth nought to me!'

'Your head will not be touched, Etin,
    Nor you hanged on a tree,
Your lady's in her father's court,
    And all he wants is thee.'

When he came in before the King,
    He fell low on his knee.
'Rise up, rise up now, Hynd Etin,
    This day ye'll dine with me.'

And as they were at dinner set,
    The wee boy thus spake he,
'I wish we were at holy kirk,
    To get us Christiantìe!'

'Your asking's not so great, my boy,
    But granted it shall be;
This day to good kirk you shall go,
    And your mother go with thee.'

But she beside the door did stand,
    When to the kirk she came,
She could not come a step within,
    She was so sunk down with shame.

Then out and spake the parish priest,
    And a sweet smile gave he:
'Come in, come in, my lily-flower,
    Present your babes to me.'
And he has ta'en and blessed them all,
    And given them Christiantìe.

Charles and Vincent, Sam and Dick,
  And likewise John and James;
They called the eldest Young Etin,
  Which was his father's name.

Lady Elspat

'How smooth's your brow, my lady Elspat!
  How golden yellow is your hair!
Of all the maids in bonny Scotland,
  There's none like lady Elspat fair!'

'Perform your vows, sweet William,' says she,
  'The vows which ye have made to me;
And at the back of my mother's castle,
  This night I'll surely meet with thee.'

199

But woe be to her brother's page,
  That heard the words between these two;
He's told them to her lady mother,
  Which wrought sweet William bitter woe.

For she has taken him, sweet William,
  And bound him with his own bow-string;
Till the red blood of his fair body
  From every nail of his hands did spring.

O it fell out upon a morning
  That the Lord Justice came to town;
And she has taken him, sweet William,
  And brought him to the Justice bound.

'And what's the crime now, lady,' says he,
  'That has by this young man been done?'
'O he has broken my bonny castle,
  That was well built with lime and stone.

'And he has broken my bonny coffers,
  That was well banded with bands of oak,
And he has stolen my rich jewels,
  Yes, every jewel from me he took.'

Then out and spake her, Lady Elspat,
  As she sat by the Justice' knee;
'Now you have told your tale, my mother,
  I pray, Lord Justice, you'll now hear me.

'He has not broken her bonny castle,
  That is well built with lime and stone;
Nor has he stolen her rich jewels,
  For I wot she has them every one.

'But though he was my first and true-love,
  And though I'd sworn to be his bride,
Since he had not great lands and money,
  She would this way our loves divide.'

Then out and spake him the Lord Justice,
   I wot the tear was in his e'e;
'I see no fault in this young William,
   Go loose his bands, and set him free.

'And take your love now, lady Elspat,
   And my best blessing you both upon;
For if he be your first and true-love,
   He is my eldest sister's son.

'There stands a good steed in my stable,
   Cost me of gold full many a pound;
You'll get as much of my free land now,
   As he in a summer's day rides round.'

Annie
of Lochroyan

'O who will shoe my bonny foot,
  And who will glove my hand,
And who will bind my middle slim
  With a long, long linen band?

'O who will comb my yellow hair
  With a new-made silver comb?
And who will be my babe's father
  Till Gregory come home?'

'Thy father he will shoe thy foot,
  Thy brother will glove thy hand,
Thy mother will bind thy middle slim
  With a long, long linen band.

'Thy sister will comb thy yellow hair
  With a new-made silver comb;
The Almighty will be thy babe's father
  Till Gregory come home.'

'O if I had a bonny ship,
  And men to sail with me,
It's I would go to my true-love,
  Since he will not come to me!'

Her father's given her a bonny ship,
  And sent her to the strand,
She's taken her young son in her arms,
  And turned her back to land.

She had not sailed but twenty leagues,
  But twenty leagues and three,
When that she saw a fair castle
  On a rock above the sea.

Says, 'Row the boat, my mariners,
  And bring me to the land,
For yonder I see my love's castle,
  Close by the salt sea strand.'

She sailed it round, and sailed it round,
  And loud and loud cried she,
'Now break, now break your fairy charms,
  And set my true-love free!'

She's ta'en her young son in her arms,
  And to the door she's gone,
And long she knocked, and sore she called,
  But answer got she none.

'O open, open, Gregory,
  O open, if you're within!
For here's the lass of Lochroyan
  Come far from kith and kin.

'O open the door, Lord Gregory,
  O open and let me in!
The wind blows loud and cold, Gregory,
  The rain drops from my chin.

'The shoe is frozen to my foot,
  The glove unto my hand,
The wet drips from my yellow hair,
  No longer can I stand.'

O up and spake his evil mother—
  And evil her death shall be!—
'You're not the lass of Lochroyan,
  She's far out o'er the sea.

'Away, away, you ill woman!
  You're not come here for good,
You're but some witch, or wild warlock,
  Or mermaid of the flood.'

'I am neither witch nor wild warlock,
  Nor mermaid of the sea,
But I am Annie of Lochroyan,
  O open the door to me!'

'If ye be Annie of Lochroyan,
  As I trow thou be not she,
Now tell me some of the love-tokens
  That passed 'tween me and thee.'

'O do not ye mind, love Gregory,
  When we sat at the wine,
How we changed the napkins from our necks?
  And I can show thee thine.

'And yours was good and good enough,
  But not so good as mine,
For yours was of the cambric clear,
  But mine of the silk so fine.

'And do ye not mind, love Gregory,
  As we sat down to dine,
How we changed the rings from our fingers?
  And I can show thee thine.

'And yours was good and good enough,
  But aye the best was mine,
For yours was of the good red gold,
  But mine of the diamond fine.

'Now open the door, love Gregory,
  Open the door, I pray!
For thy young son is in my arms,
  And will be dead ere day.'

'Away, away, you ill woman,
  Go from my door for shame!
For I have gotten another fair love,
  So you may hie you home.'

Fair Annie turned her round about:
  'Well, if it must be so,
May never a woman that's born a son
  Have a heart so full of woe!'

O softly, softly went she back,
  As the day began to peep;
She set her foot on good ship-board,
  And sore, sore did she weep.

When the cock had crowed, and the day had dawned,
  And the sun began to peep,
Up then rose Lord Gregory
  Out of his drowsy sleep.

'O I have dreamed a dream, mother,
  I wish it may bring good!
That the bonny lass of Lochroyan
  At my bower window stood.

'O I have dreamed a dream, mother,
  The thought o't makes me weep!
That fair Annie of Lochroyan
  Lay dead at my bed-feet.'

'If it be for Annie of Lochroyan
  That you make all this moan,
She stood last night at your bower-door,
  But I have sent her home.'

'O woe betide you, ill woman,
  And ill may your death be!
That would not open the door yourself,
  Nor yet would waken me!'

O quickly, quickly rose he up,
  And fast ran to the strand,
And there he saw her, fair Annie,
  Was sailing from the land.

And it's 'Hey Annie!' and 'How Annie!
  O Annie, will ye not bide?'
But aye the more that he cried 'Annie!'
  The faster ran the tide.

And it's 'Hey Annie!' and 'How Annie!
  O Annie, speak to me!'
But aye the louder he cried 'Annie!'
  The louder roared the sea.

The wind blew loud, the waves rose high
  And dashed the boat on shore;
Fair Annie's corpse was in the foam,
  The babe rose never more.

Lord Gregory tore his golden locks
  And made a woeful moan;
Fair Annie's corpse lay at his feet,
  Her bonny son was gone.

'O cherry, cherry was her cheek,
  And golden was her hair,
And coral, coral was her lips,
  None might with her compare.'

Then first he kissed her pale, pale cheek,
  And next he kissed her chin,
And next he kissed her wan, wan lips,
  There was no breath within.

'O woe betide thee, my cruel mother,
  An ill death come to thee!
You turned my true-love from my door,
  Who died for love of me!'

The Lochmabyn Harper

O heard ye not of the silly blind Harper,
　　How he lived long in Lochmabyn town,
And how he would go to fair England,
　　To steal King Henry's Wanton Brown?

But first he went to his good wife,
　　He went with all the haste he might,
'Without a mare that has a foal,'
　　Says he, 'this work will ne'er go right.'

'Thou hast a good grey mare to run
　　O'er hills both low and high,' says she;
'So set thee on the grey mare's back,
　　And leave the foal at home with me.

'And take a halter in thy hose,
　　And of thy purpose do not fail,
But wrap it round the Wanton's nose,
　　And tie him to the grey mare's tail.'

So he is up to England gone,
　　Even as fast as fast can be,
And when he came to Carlisle gate,
　　O who was there but King Henrỳ?

'Come into my hall, thou silly blind Harper,
    And of thy harping let me hear!'
'O, by my sooth,' says the silly blind Harper,
    'I'd rather have stabling for my mare.'

The King looks over his left shoulder,
    And says unto his stable groom,
'Go take the silly blind Harper's mare,
    And tie her beside my Wanton Brown.'

Then aye he harpèd, and aye he carpèd,
    Till all the lordlings footed the floor;
They thought the music was so sweet,
    That they forgot the stable door.

And aye he harpèd, and aye he carpèd,
    Till all the nobles were sound asleep,
Then quietly he took off his shoes,
    And softly down the stair did creep.

Then to the stable door he hies,
    With tread as light as light could be;
And when he opened and went in,
    There he found thirty steeds and three.

He took the halter from his hose,
    And of his purpose did not fail,
He slipped it o'er the Wanton's nose,
    And tied it to the grey mare's tail.

He turned them loose at the castle gate,
    O'er moor and moss and every dale,
And she ne'er let the Wanton wait,
    But kept him going at her tail.

The mare she was right swift of foot,
    She did not fail to find the way,
For she was at Lochmabyn gate,
    Full long three hours before the day.

O she gave many a snicker and snort
   At the Harper's door when she got there:
'Rise up,' says the wife, 'thou lazy lass,
   Let in thy master and his mare.'

Then up she rose, put on her clothes,
   And she looked out through the lock-hole:
'O, by my sooth,' then cries the lass,
   'Our mare has got a fine brown foal!'

'Come hold thy tongue, thou foolish lass!
   'Tis but the moon deceiving thee,
I'll bet my wealth against a groat
   He's bigger than e'er our foal will be.'

Now all this while in merry Carlisle
   The Harper harpèd to high and low,
And what could they do but listen him to,
   Until that the cock began to crow?

But on the morn at fair daylight,
   When they had ended all their cheer,
Behold the Wanton Brown was gone,
   And eke the poor blind Harper's mare.

'Alas, alas!' says the silly blind Harper
   'And ever alas that I came here,
In Scotland I've lost a fine colt-foal,
   In England they've stolen my good grey mare!'

'Come! cease thy "alasing", thou silly blind Harper,
   And again of thy harping let us hear;
And well-paid shall thy colt-foal be,
   And thou shalt have a far better mare.'

Then aye he harpèd, and aye he carpèd,
   So sweet were the harpings he let them hear!
He was paid for the foal he had never lost,
   And three times o'er for the good grey mare.

Clerk Colven

Clerk Colven and his gay lady,
  As they walked in yon garden green,
The belt about her middle slim
  It cost Clerk Colven crowns fifteen.

'O hearken well now, my good lord,
  O hearken well to what I said;
When you go to the Well of Stream
  O go not near the lovely maid.'

'O hold your tongue, my gay lady,
  Now speak no more of that to me,
For I ne'er saw a fair woman
  That I could like as well as thee.'

He's mounted on his berry-brown steed,
  And merry, merry rode he on,
Till that he came to the Well of Stream,
  And there he saw the mermaidèn.

'Ye wash, ye wash, ye bonny maid,
  And aye ye wash your smock of silk.'
'It's all for ye, you gentle knight,
  My skin is whiter than the milk.'

He's taken her by the milk-white hand,
  He's taken her by the sleeve so green,
And he's forgotten his gay lady,
  And he's away with the mermaidèn.

'Ohone, alas!' says Clerk Colven,
  'And aye so sore it aches my head!'
And merrily laughed the mermaiden,
  'O 'twill ache on till you be dead.

'But out ye take your little pen-knife,
   And from my smock ye cut a gore;
Wrap that about your bonny head,
   And the pain ye'll never feel no more.

Out he has ta'en his little pen-knife,
   And from her smock he's cut a gore;
She's tied it round his whey-white face,
   But aye his head it ached the more.

'Ohone, alas!' said Clerk Colven,
   'O sorer, sorer aches my head!'
'And sorer, sorer ever will,
   And aye be worse till ye be dead.'

213

Then out he drew his shining blade,
    And thought with that to kill her dead,
But she became a fish again,
    And merrily sprang into the flood.

He's mounted on his berry-brown steed,
    And doleful, doleful rode he home,
And heavily, heavily lighted down,
    When to his lady's bower he's come.

'O mother, mother make my bed,
    And, gentle lady, lay me down,
O brother, brother unbend my bow,
    'Twill never be bent by me again!'

His mother she has made his bed,
    His gentle lady laid him down,
His brother he has unbent his bow—
    'Twas never bent by him again.

Annan Water

'Annan water's deep to wade,
    And my love Annie's wondrous bonny;
Loath am I she should wet her feet,
    Because I love her best of any.

'Go saddle me the bonny black,
    Go saddle soon, and make him ready;
For I will down the Gatehope-Slack,
    And all to see my bonny lady.'

He's leapt upon the bonny black,
  And stirred him with the spur right sorely;
But ere he won the Gatehope-Slack,
  I think the steed was woe and weary.

He's leaped upon the bonny grey,
  He rode the right way and the ready,
I trow he would neither stop nor stay,
  For he was seeking his bonny lady.

O he has ridden o'er field and fell,
  Through moor, and moss, and many a mire,
His spurs of steel were sore to bide,
  And from her fore-feet flew the fire.

'My bonny grey now play your part,
  If you be the steed that wins my dearie,
With corn and hay you'll aye be fed,
  And never spur shall make you weary!'

The grey was a mare, and a right good mare,
    But when she won the Annan water,
She couldn't have ridden a furlong more,
    Had a thousand marks been wagered on her.

'O boatman, boatman, put off your boat,
    Put off your boat for golden money!
I cross the drumly stream tonight,
    Or never more I see my honey!'

'O I was sworn so late yestreen,
    And not by one oath, but by many;
And for all the gold in fair Scotland,
    I dare not take you through to Annie.'

The side was steep, and the bottom deep,
    From bank to brae the water pouring;
And the bonny grey mare did sweat with fear,
    For she heard the water-kelpie roaring.

O he has pulled off his diapered coat,
    The silver buttons glancèd bonny,
The waistcoat bursted off his breast,
    He was so full of melancholy.

He has taken the ford at that stream tail,
    I wot he swam both strong and steady,
But the stream was broad, and his strength did fail,
    And he never saw his bonny lady.

'O woe betide the brittle willow-wand,
    And woe betide the bush of briar,
It broke into my true love's hand,
    When his strength did fail, and his limbs did tire.

'And woe betide you, Annan water,
    This night that ye are a drumly river!
For over thee I'll build a bridge,
    That ye no more true love may sever.'

The Duke of Gordon's Daughter

The Duke of Gordon had three daughters,
  Elizabeth, Margret and Jean;
They would not stay in bonny castle Gordon,
  But they went to bonny Aberdeen.

They had not been in bonny Aberdeen
  A twelvemonth and a day,
Lady Jean fell in love with Captain Ogilvìe,
  And would go with him away.

Word came to the Duke of Gordon,
  In chamber where he lay,
Lady Jean was in love with Captain Ogilvìe,
  And from him she would not stay.

'Go saddle me the black, black horse,
  And you'll ride on the grey,
And I will go to bonny Aberdeen,
  To bring Lady Jean away.'

They were not a mile from bonny Aberdeen,
  A mile but barely one,
Till he met with his two daughters walking,
  But Lady Jean was gone.

'Where is your sister, maidens,
  Where is your sister now,
Where is your sister, maidens,
  That she is not walking with you?'

'O pardon us, honoured father,
  O pardon us we pray!
Lady Jean is wed with Captain Ogilvìe,
  And from him she will not stay.'

The Duke did frown and the Duke rode on
  Till he came to bonny Aberdeen,
And there he did see brave Captain Ogilvìe,
  A-training of his men on the green.

'O woe be to thee, thou Captain Ogilvìe,
  And an ill death shalt thou die!
For taking to thee my daughter Jean,
  Thou shalt be hanged on high!'

Duke Gordon has written a broad letter,
  To the King a letter wrote he;
It was if ever he hanged a man,
  To hang brave Captain Ogilvìe.

'I will not hang brave Captain Ogilvìe,
  For no duke that I see;
But I'll make him put off the scarlet and the lace,
  And a private soldier he shall be.'

In chamber where he was lying,
  Word came to Captain Ogilvìe,
To put off the gold-lace and scarlet,
  And put on a private's liverỳ.

'If this be for bonny Jeanie Gordon,
  This penance I'll take and more;
If this be for bonny Jeanie Gordon,
  This will I gladly endure!'

Lady Jean had not been married,
  Not a year but barely three,
Till she had a babe on every arm,
  Another on her knee.

'O but I'm weary of wandering!
  O but my fortune is bad!
It becomes not the Duke of Gordon's daughter
  To follow a soldier lad.

'O but I'm weary, weary wandering!
  O but 'tis long to me!
It becomes not the Duke of Gordon's daughter
  A soldier lad's wife for to be!'

'O hold thy tongue, Jeanie Gordon,
  O hold thy tongue, my lamb;
For once I was a noble, noble captain,
  Now for thy sake a soldier lad I am.'

When they came to the Highland hills,
  Cold was the frost and snow;
Lady Jean's shoes they were all torn,
  No farther could she go.

'Woe to the hills and the mountains!
   Woe to the wind and the rain!
My feet are so sore with going barefoot,
   I cannot walk for the pain.

'O if I were at the glens of Foudlen,
   Where hunting I oft have gone,
I could find my way to bonny Castle Gordon,
   And get hosen and shoes to put on.'

When she came to bonny Castle Gordon,
   And standing on the green,
The porter out with a loud, loud shout,
   'O here comes our Lady Jean!'

'You are welcome, bonny Jeanie Gordon,
   You are dear welcome to me;
You are welcome, dear Jeanie Gordon,
   But away with your Captain Ogilvìe!'

Over seas now went the Captain,
   As a soldier under command;
But a message soon followed after,
   To come home and inherit his land.

'Come home, you pretty Captain Ogilvie,
   Come home and heir your brother's land;
Come home, you pretty Captain Ogilvie,
   Be Earl of Cumberland.'

'O what does this mean?' says the Captain,
   'Where's my brother's children three?'
'They are all of them dead and buried,
   And the lands they are ready for thee.'

'Then hoist up your sails,' says the Captain,
   'And we'll hie back o'er the sea;
And I'll go to bonny Castle Gordon,
   There my dear Jeanie to see.'

He came to bonny Castle Gordon,
  And on the green stood he:
The porter out with a loud, loud shout,
  'Here comes our Captain Ogilvie!'

'You're welcome, pretty Captain Ogilvie,
  Your fortune's advanced, I hear;
No stranger can come to my castle
  That I do love so dear.'

'Put up your hat, Duke of Gordon,
  Let it not fall from your head.
It becomes not the noble Duke of Gordon
  To bow to a private soldier lad!

'Sir, the last time I was at your castle,
  You would not let me in;
I'm come for my wife and children,
  No friendship else to win.'

'Come in, come in, pretty Captain Ogilvie,
  And drink of the beer and the wine;
And thou shalt have gold and silver,
  To count till the clock strikes nine.'

'I'll have none of your gold and silver,
  Nor none of your white money;
But I'll have my bonny Jeanie Gordon,
  And she shall now go with me.'

Down the stair Lady Jean came tripping,
  With the salt tear in her e'e;
She had a babe in every arm,
  And another at her knee.

'You're welcome, my bonny Jeanie Gordon,
  Dear welcome you are to me!
You're welcome, dear Jeanie Gordon,
  My Countess of Cumberland to be!'

The Fair Flower of Northumberland

It was a knight in Scotland born
  Follow, my love, come over the strand—
Was taken a prisoner and left forlorn,
  By the good Earl of Northumberland.

There he was cast into prison strong,
  Follow, my love, come over the strand—
Where he could not walk nor lie along,
  Even by the good Earl of Northumberland.

And as in sorrow thus he lay,
  Follow, my love, come over the strand—
The Earl's sweet daughter walked that way,
  And she the fair flower of Northumberland.

And loud to her this knight did cry,
  Follow, my love, come over the strand—
The salt tears standing in his eye,
  And she the fair flower of Northumberland.

'Fair lady,' he said, 'take pity on me,
  Follow, my love, come over the strand—
To die in prison leave not me,
  And you the fair flower of Northumberland.'

'Fair sir, how should I take pity on thee?
  Follow, my love, come over the strand—
Thou being a foe to our country,
  And I the fair flower of Northumberland?'

'Fair lady, I am no foe,' he said,
Follow, my love, come over the strand—
Through thy sweet love here was I stayed,
    For thee, the fair flower of Northumberland.'

'Why shouldst thou come here for love of me,
Follow, my love, come over the strand—
Having wife and children in thy countrỳ,
    And I the fair flower of Northumberland?'

'I swear by Him that was crowned with thorn,
Follow, my love, come over the strand—
That I never had wife since the day I was born,
    And I'll make you my lady in fair Scotlànd.'

She stole from her father's pillow the key,
Follow, my love, come over the strand—
And soon out of prison she's set him free
    To wend with her into fair Scotlànd.

Likewise much gold she got by sleight,
Follow, my love, come over the strand—
And all to help this fòrlorn knight
    To go from her father to fair Scotlànd.

She's led him down to her father's stable,
Follow, my love, come over the strand—
And she's stolen two steeds both strong and able,
    To carry them on into fair Scotlànd.

They rode till they came to a water clear,
Follow, my love, come over the strand—
'Good sir, how shall I follow you here?
    And I the fair flower of Northumberland!

'The water is rough and wonderful steep,
Follow, my love, come over the strand—
And on my saddle I shall not keep,
    And I the fair flower of Northumberland!'

'Fear not the ford, fair lady,' said he,
 Follow, my love, come over the strand—
For longer I cannot stay for thee,
  Though thou be the fair flower of Northumber-
   land.'

From top to toe all wet was she,
 Follow, my love, come over the strand—
'This have I done for love of thee,
  And I the fair flower of Northumberland!'

They rode till they came to a Scottish moss,
 Follow, my love, come over the strand—
He bade her light off from her father's horse,
  Says, 'Go you back to Northumberland.

'For I have a wife and children five,
  Follow, my love, come over the strand—
In Edinburgh they be alive,
  So get thee home to Northumberland.'

'Have pity on me, as I had it on thee,
  Follow, my love, come over the strand—
A cook in your kitchen I will be,
  Even I, the fair flower of Northumberland!

'Or take me up by the body so meek,
  Follow, my love, come over the strand—
And throw me into the water deep,
  For I dare not go back to Northumberland.'

He turned him around and he thought of a plan,
  Follow, my love, come over the strand—
He bought an old horse and he hired an old man,
  To carry her back to Northumberland.

When she came through her father's hall,
  Follow, my love, come over the strand—
She bowed her down low before them all,
  She was the fair flower of Northumberland.

Down came her father, he saw her and smiled,
  Follow, my love, come over the strand—
'You are not the first the false Scots have beguiled,
  And you're aye welcome back to Northumberland!'

The Old Cloak

This winter's weather it waxeth cold,
    And frost it freezeth on every hill,
And Boreas blows his blast so bold
    That all our cattle are like to spill.
Bell, my wife, she loves no strife;
    She said unto me quietly,
'Rise up, and save cow Crumbock's life!
    Man, put thine old cloak about thee!'

He. 'O Bell, my wife, why dost thou chide?
    Thou knowest my cloak is very thin;
It is so bare and overworn,
    An insect could not hide therein.
Then I'll no longer borrow nor lend,
    For once I'll new apparelled be;
Tomorrow I'll to town and spend,
    For I'll have a new cloak about me.'

She. 'Cow Crumbock is a very good cow,
    She has been ever true to the pail,
She has helped us to butter and cheese, I trow,
    And other things she will not fail.
I would be loath to see her pine.
    Good husband, counsel take of me:
It's not for us to go so fine—
    Man, take thine old cloak about thee!'

He. 'My cloak it was a very good cloak,
    It hath been always true to the wear,
But now it is not worth a groat,
    I have had it four and forty year.
Sometime it was of cloth in grain,
    'Tis now but a dish clout, as you may see;
It will hold out neither wind nor rain,
    And I'll have a new cloak about me.'

She. 'It is four and forty years ago
 Since the one of us the other did ken;
And we have had, betwixt us two,
 Of children either nine or ten.
We have brought them up to be women and men;
 In the fear of God I trow they be:
And why wilt thou thyself mis-ken?
 Man, take thine old cloak about thee!'

227

He. 'O Bell my wife, why dost thou chide?
 Now is now, and then was then;
Seek now all the country wide,
 Thou kens not clowns from gentlemen.
They are clad in black, green, yellow and blue,
 So far above their own degree.
Once in my life I'll take a view,
 For I'll have a new cloak about me.'

She. King Stephen was a worthy peer,
 His breeches cost him but a crown;
He held them sixpence all too dear,
 Therefore he called the tailor "lown"
He was a king and wore a crown,
 And thou art but of low degree.
It's pride that puts this country down;
 Man, take thy old cloak about thee!'

Bell, my wife, she loves not strife,
 Yet she will lead me, if she can:
And to maintain an easy life,
 I oft must yield, though I'm good-man.
It's not for a man with a woman to scrap,
 Unless he first give o'er the plea:
As we began, so will we keep,
 And I'll take my old cloak about me.

Hynd Horn

Hynd Horn's bound, love, and Hynd Horn's free,
'O where were ye born, and in what countrỳ?'

'In the good green-wood, there was I born,
And all my forbears me beforn.'

Seven long years he served the king,
And all for the sake of his daughter Jean.

229

The king an angry man was he,
And he sent young Hynd Horn to the sea.

He's given his love a silver wand,
With seven silver laverocks sitting thereon.

She's given him a gay gold ring,
With seven bright diamonds set therein.

'As long's these diamonds keep their hue,
Ye'll know I am a lover true;

But when the ring turns pale and wan,
Ye may know I'm pledged to another man.'

He hoist up his sails and away sailed he,
Until he came to a foreign countrỳ.

One day as he looked his ring upon,
He saw the diamonds pale and wan.

He's left the seas and he's come to land,
And the first he met was an old beggar man.

'What news, what news, thou old beggar man?
For it's seven long years since I've seen this land.'

'No news,' said the beggar, 'no news at all,
But there's a wedding in the king's hall.'

'Cast off, cast off thy old beggar weed,
And I'll give thee my good grey steed.

'And lend to me your wig of hair
To cover mine, because it is fair.'

'My begging weed is not for thee,
Your riding steed is not for me.'

But part by right and part by wrong,
Hynd Horn has changed with the beggar man.

The beggar man was bound for to ride,
But young Hynd Horn was bound for the bride.

When he came to the king's gate,
He asked a drink for Hynd Horn's sake;

The bride came tripping down the stair,
With combs of red-gold in her hair.

She'd a cup of red wine in her hand,
And that she gave to the beggar man.

He's taken the wine and he's drunk it up,
And the ring he's dropped into the cup

'O got ye this by sea or land,
Or got ye it off a dead man's hand?'

'I got it not by sea nor land,
But I got it, madam, from your own hand.'

'O I'll cast off my silken gown,
And I'll follow you from town to town.

'O I'll take the gold combs from my head,
And I'll follow you to beg my bread.'

'Keep on, keep on your combs,' he said,
'You need not take them from your head.'

Then down he let his ragged cloak fall,
And the red gold shinèd over him all.

O the bridegroom thought the lady to wed.
But young Hynd Horn got her instead.

Katherine Johnstone

There was a maid, and a well-favoured maid,
   Lived high up in yon glen,
Her name was Katherine Johnstone,
   She was courted by many men.

Down came the Laird of Lamington
   Out of the North Countrỳ,
All for to court this pretty maid,
   Her bridegroom for to be.

He telled not her father, he telled not her mother,
   He telled not one of her kin;
But he telled the bonny lass herself,
   And her consent did win.

But up then came Lord Faughanwood,
   Out from the English Border,
And for to court this pretty maid,
   All mounted in good order.

He's telled her father, he's telled her mother,
   And all the rest of her kin,
But he's telled not the bonny lass herself,
   Till on her wedding-e'en.

She's sent unto her first dear love,
   If he would come to see,
And Lamington has sent back word
   Well answered should she be.

Then he has sent a messenger
   Right quietly through the land,
For four-and-twenty armèd men,
   To ride at his command.

The bridegroom from the high window
  Beheld both dale and down,
And there he spied her first dear love
  Come riding to the town.

She scoffèd him, and she scornèd him
  Upon her wedding day,
And said it was the Fairy Court
  He saw in such array!

When all were at the dinner set,
  Drinking the blood-red wine,
In came the Laird of Lamington,
  The bridegroom should have been.

'O come ye here to fight, young lord,
  Or come ye here to play,
Or come ye here to drink good wine,
  Upon the wedding day?'

'I come not here to fight,' he said,
  'I come not here to play,
I'll but lead a dance with the bonny bride,
  And mount and ride away.'

There was a glass of the blood-red wine,
  Was filled them up between,
But aye she drank to Lamington,
  Who her true love had been.

He's ta'en her by the milk-white hand,
  And by the grass-green sleeve,
He's mounted her high behind himself,
  Of her kin he's asked no leave.

There were four-and-twenty bonny boys,
  All clad in Johnstone grey,
They swore they would take the bride again
  By the strong hand, if they may.

It's up, it's up the Cowden bank,
  It's down the Cowden brae,
The bride she caused the trumpet sound,
  'It is a well-won play!'

The blood ran down by Cowden bank,
  And down by Cowden brae,
But aye she caused the trumpet sound,
  'It's all fair play!'

'My blessing on your heart, sweet thing,
  Woe to your wilful will!
So many a gallant gentleman's blood
  This day you've caused to spill!

'But all you lords of fair England,
  If you be English born,
Come never to Scotland to seek a wife,
  Or else you'll get the scorn.

'They'll hold you up, and put you by,
  Until your wedding day;
They'll give you frogs instead of fish,
  And do you foul, foul play.'

A Lyke-Wake Dirge

This ae night, this ae night,
Every night and all,
Fire and sleet and candlelight,
And Christ receive thy soul.

When thou from hence away art past,
Every night and all,
To Whinny-Moor thou com'st at last,
And Christ receive thy soul.

If ever thou gavest hosen and shoon,
Every night and all,
Sit thee down and put them on,
And Christ receive thy soul.

If hosen and shoon thou never gav'st none,
Every night and all,
The whins shall prick thee to the bare bone,
And Christ receive thy soul.

From Whinny-Moor when thou art past,
Every night and all,
To Bridge of Dread thou com'st at last,
And Christ receive thy soul.

From Bridge of Dread when thou art past,
Every night and all,
To Purgatory fire thou com'st at last,
And Christ receive thy soul.

If ever thou gavest meat and drink,
Every night and all,
The fire shall never make thee shrink,
And Christ receive thy soul.

If meat and drink thou never gav'st none,
   Every night and all,
The fire shall burn thee to the bare bone,
   And Christ receive thy soul.

This ae night, this ae night,
   Every night and all,
Fire and sleet and candlelight,
   And Christ receive thy soul.

Glossary

ABOON Above
AE (This ae night) This very night
AN If
ANNOY Grief
BAGS OF BREAD Bags carried by beggars for food, etc.
BALE Evil
BAN-DOG A large fierce dog
BANE Woe; grief; ruin
BENT Heath; rough grass
BICKER Skirmish; run about
BILLIE Brother
BILLY BLIND Household fairy; brownie
BIRK Birch
BONE (royal bone) Ivory
BOOT Good; advantage
BRAE Steep bank; hillside
BRAND Sword
BREEKS Breeches
BROAD (of a letter) Open (not rolled up and sealed)
BURD Maiden
BURN Stream
CARE (I have no care of) I am not worried about
CARLINE Old woman
CARP Sing or recite (as a minstrel)
CATCHIPOLL Sheriff's officer
CHANNERING Complaining; grumbling
CLOTH IN GRAIN Scarlet cloth
CLOUGH Cliff; glen between steep banks
CORBIE Raven
CURTAL Cut short, as of a garment, an animal's tail, etc. The
    Curtal Friar is the famous Friar Tuck. (*Tuck* because his habit
    was *tucked* up by a girdle)
CURTAL-DOG A dog with a docked tail
DEMESNE Estate
DOLE Grief
DREE Suffer
DRUMLY Turbid; troubled; tumultuous
DYKE Ditch
E'E Eye
E'EN Eyes

239

E'EN Evening
EKE Also
EVERMAIR Ever more
FAIN Willing
FEE Possessions; money
FELL Mountain
FINIKIN Fine and neat
FORLORN Utterly lost
FYTTE A section of a poem
GIN The trick of the door latch
GLAMOUR Spell; magic
GRAMARYE Magic
GRAMERCY Thank you very much
GREASE Fat
GRUMLY Gruesome
GURLY Rough; stormy
HABIT Clothes
HARP AND CARP Play and recite or sing
HOLYDAME Halidom; holiness; a holy relic
HOSEN Hose; stockings
HYND Serving man
INN (noun) Stand
KEN Know
KNIFE-AND-SHEARLESS Without knife or scissors
LAVEROCK Skylark
LEVEN Lawn; smooth grassy place
LIDDEL-RACK A ford over the river Liddel
LIGHT Alight
LINN Waterfall
LIST Desire; inclination
LYKE Body
LYKE-WAKE A watching by the dead
MAHOUND Mohammed
MAIR More
MEET Narrow
MICKLE Great
MIND Remember
MIS-KEN (thyself) Not know yourself
MORT A flourish of the hunting horn at the death of a deer
MOSS A moor covered with peat moss
MOTHER-NAKED Stark-naked
MURK Dark

MYSELL Myself
MYSTERY Handicraft
NEAT HORN A horn blown to call out the townsfolk (literally a cattle horn)
NEEDLE-THREADLESS Without needle or thread
PARAMOUR Lover
PAYNIM Pagan
PIT MURK Black as the pit
PRIME 6 a.m.
PROPER Real; true
RAKING Advancing swiftly
RANGER Keeper of a royal park
RATTENS Rats
ROUND (of a bowstring) Not frayed
RUTH Pity
SCRIP Wallet; satchel
SEE (save and see) Protect
SHEEN Shining; radiant
SHINING (verb) Moving along with the light shimmering on one
SHOON Shoes
SHOT Reckoning; bill
SHRIFT Confession
SILKIE Seal
SKEELY Skilful
SLACK A steep slope
SNELL Cold; keen
SNICKER Whinny
SPAN Nine inches
THRONG (verb) Hurried
TIDE Time
TREE Wood; the Cross
TROW Believe; think
TRYST (verb) Make an appointment to meet
       (noun) An appointment to meet
TRYSTING TREE A special tree in the forest where hunters meet and keep a store of weapons, etc.
UNCOUTH Queer; outlandish
WAN Dark; black
WANTON Spoilt; wilful
WARE Aware
WARELY Cautiously
WARLOCK Wizard

WATER-KELPIE A wicked water-sprite
WEAL Good fortune
WEEDS Clothes
WEND Go
WHIN Gorse
WICKER Willow
WIS Know
WIST Know; known
WOT Know
WROTH Angry
YESTREEN Yesterday evening; last night

Index of first lines